ORGANIC CHEMISTRY:
A CONTEMPORARY VIEW

PAUL L. COOK

PROFESSOR OF CHEMISTRY
ALBION COLLEGE

JOHN W. CRUMP

PROFESSOR OF CHEMISTRY
ALBION COLLEGE

Printed in the United States of America.

Library of Congress Number 77-79289

D. C. HEATH AND COMPANY
A Division of Raytheon Education Company
Lexington, Massachusetts

Preface

This book serves to introduce the manner in which one field of chemistry, organic chemistry, utilizes and extends the basic concepts which underlie other fields of chemistry. It is expected that the book will be used principally by college undergraduates as a supplement to a general chemistry textbook. It is therefore assumed that the reader is familiar with many of the principles treated in general chemistry textbooks, particularly the concepts of atomic structure, covalent bonding, orbital hybridization, electronegativity, and the relationship between bonding and structure.

The enormous breadth of the field of organic chemistry precludes the possibility of a comprehensive introduction to the subject, even at a very elementary level, within the scope of this book. An attempt has been made to deal with as many of the basic concepts of organic chemistry as possible, while limiting the illustration or application of these concepts to a few selected systems. In the choice of examples, attention has been given to those areas in other fields, particularly biology and polymer chemistry, which are dependent upon organic chemistry.

Presented with any new problem involving a compound, the organic chemist tends to think first in terms of molecular structure, then of properties and reactions associated with that structure, and finally of series of reactions involving the structure (synthesis). This sequence of steps comprises the basic format of this book (Chapters 2–6), following an introductory chapter which begins with a brief description of the discoveries from which organic chemistry emerged as a distinct discipline and concludes with some of the frontier areas of current research in organic chemistry.

After a brief review of the principles of covalent bonding, Chapter 2 analyzes the existence of a virtually infinite array of organic compounds in terms of the uniqueness of the key element, carbon, and the concepts of isomerism and functional groups. A discussion of the relationship between physical properties and molecular structure (Chapter 3) is followed, in Chapter 4, by one in which these properties are used in the determination of structure. The student is introduced to the general procedure used by an organic chemist in the isolation, purification, and ultimate assignment of a structural formula to an unknown compound. The classical methods of separation and purification are discussed along with the modern analytical tools—infrared, NMR, and mass spectroscopy, as well as the chromatographic techniques. Chapter 5 describes three important types of organic reactions (addition, elimination, and substitution) and some of the mechanisms by which these reactions are thought to occur. The focus is upon the similarity of simple bond-forming and bond-breaking steps and the importance of reaction intermediates as a means of organizing the vast number of organic reactions into related groups. The synthetic application of organic reactions is then discussed in an attempt to provide an understanding of and an appreciation for the problems involved in the conception, design, and experimental execution of a successful synthesis. The final chapter examines the manner in which the threads of structure, analysis, reactions, and synthesis converge in a particular area—that of macromolecules. Attention is focused on the structural features of natural and synthetic polymers and the progress which has been made in structure determination and synthesis.

We wish to express our indebtedness to Professors John C. Bailar and Jacob Kleinberg, who carefully read the entire manuscript and offered many helpful suggestions and to Professor Dorothy Ingalls of Albion College, who assisted us greatly in the proofreading with her thorough attention to detail. We also wish to thank Dr. Paul Bryant, editor, for assisting us through the tedious tasks that face all authors, and the sources who kindly provided illustrative material. Finally, we express our appreciation to our families who not only encouraged us in this undertaking but bore with understanding the additional demands upon the authors' time.

Albion College,   *Paul L. Cook*
Albion, Michigan   *John W. Crump*

Contents

CHAPTER 1

Introduction:
The Nature of Organic Chemistry

DEFINITIONS

The academic discipline of chemistry is frequently divided into five classifications—*inorganic* chemistry, *organic* chemistry, *analytical* chemistry, *physical* chemistry, and *biochemistry*. Inorganic chemistry is generally conceded to include the chemistry of all elements other than carbon whose unique properties are covered in the area of organic chemistry. Analytical chemistry, as its name implies, deals with the qualitative and quantitative methods for the determination of the composition of matter. Physical chemistry is a study of the physical properties of matter and the correlation of these properties with chemical transformations. Biochemistry embraces the chemistry of living systems such as those found in plants and animals.

It is well for us to remember that this classification is somewhat historical in origin and, in recent years, has lost much of its significance. These subject areas of chemistry often merge and overlap and the student may find that these boundaries are no longer recognized in the chemistry curriculum in which he is enrolled. Moreover, as the science of chemistry continues to expand, more categories of specialization will necessarily evolve. Such terms as polymer chemistry, nuclear chemistry, food chemistry, radiochemistry, to name only a few, are in common use in chemical journals.

For our purposes in this book organic chemistry will refer to that branch of chemistry devoted to the chemistry of carbon compounds.

1

HISTORY AND DEVELOPMENT OF ORGANIC CHEMISTRY

Most science historians trace the pioneer period of organic chemistry to the beginning of the 19th century. At this time it was recognized that chemical compounds derived from living material all contained carbon and hydrogen. Indeed, the accepted definition of organic chemistry was that branch of chemistry which dealt with compounds obtained from plant and animal sources. It was quite natural to assume that, since organic substances were isolated from living organisms, they also possessed an additional distinguishing quality— an essential "vital force."

In 1828 the German chemist, Wöhler, published a paper which reported the thermal conversion of ammonium cyanate to urea. Urea had previously been obtained only from urine whereas ammonium cyanate could be made from nonorganic materials. This experiment was a truly significant one in the history of organic chemistry as it clearly demonstrated the interconversion of organic and inorganic substances. However, as with most well established ideas, chemists were reluctant to abandon the vitalistic theory and it was not until additional, similar experiments had been performed that this theory was eventually discarded during the middle of the 19th century. A fascinating account of the decline of vitalistic theory and the rise of structural theory is contained in reference (1).

Advances in quantitative techniques during this early period also contributed significantly to the development of organic chemistry. Methods for accurate carbon and hydrogen analysis developed by Gay-Lussac and Liebig and the Dumas method for nitrogen determination greatly improved the procedures by which empirical and molecular formulas were obtained. As the number of organic compounds increased it was soon recognized by the Swedish chemist Berzelius that compounds with different properties could have identical compositions. Berzelius proposed the term *isomer* to describe compounds of this type.

In 1859 when Kekulé and Couper independently introduced the concept of chemical bonds between atoms, they established the foundations for the structural theory of organic chemistry. They proposed that individual atoms had the same combining capacity, or valence, in different compounds. The idea of the bonding between carbon atoms

---

(1) O. T. Benfey, *From Vital Force to Structural Theory*, Houghton Mifflin Co., New York, 1964.

made possible the prediction of larger and more complex molecules. Though our modern concepts of chemical bonding may be more sophisticated, it is a tribute to these men that many of the same structural ideas which they suggested are still in use over one hundred years later. Shortly after the discoveries of Kekulé and Couper, the concept of the tetrahedral carbon atom was introduced by van't Hoff and Le Bel, extending the structural theory to the three dimensional scale.

Perhaps the modern era of organic chemistry dawned with the introduction of the electronic theory of bonding by G. N. Lewis. Lewis described the covalent bond as a pair of shared electrons between atoms, a view which related chemical bonding to atomic structure.

We are presently in an era when knowledge in organic chemistry is being accumulated at an unprecedented pace. It has been estimated that ninety per cent of all scientists who have ever lived are alive today and that the amount of scientific knowledge is doubling approximately every eight years. Chemists today are interested not only in the structure of molecules but in how and why molecules react, that is, the pathways by which reactions occur. The modern chemist is endowed with research tools and techniques in unparalleled number. Spectrophotometric instrumentation has reduced the analytical problems of the organic chemist to such an extent that problems which formerly required years of study can now be resolved in a matter of minutes or hours. Chromatographic techniques for isolation, purification, and identification have made possible the elucidation of the structures of such complex molecules as insulin, hemoglobin, and other naturally occurring macromolecules. Organic synthesis, the building of complex molecules from simpler ones, has been refined to the point where it is now possible to synthesize the intricate chlorophyll molecule, a feat once considered improbable.

IMPORTANCE OF ORGANIC CHEMISTRY

It is difficult for us to imagine an existence devoid of the many contributions made by organic chemists to our daily living. Such common organic substances as synthetic fabrics, paints and dyes, plastics of all kinds, medicines, insecticides and fertilizers have helped to make the chemical industry the fifth largest industry in the United States (based on sales).

CHAPTER 2

Structural Theory of Organic Chemistry

INTRODUCTION

Chemistry has been called one of man's great attempts to make sense out of the vast, buzzing confusion which surrounds him. It would be hard to quarrel with the aptness of this statement as applied to organic chemistry, for the organic chemist is confronted by an almost unimaginable number of compounds, displaying a remarkable range of chemical and physical properties. The first step in an attempt to introduce order into this area of buzzing confusion is to understand the way in which atoms are combined into molecules in those substances which we call organic compounds. This topic, molecular structure, is the subject of this chapter. In later chapters, we will find that an attempt is always made to relate properties of organic compounds, both physical and chemical, to their molecular structure, so that a sound understanding of this topic is essential. For a more detailed discussion of molecular structure, see reference (1).

For all their variety, organic compounds are composed of only a handful of the 103 known elements. In addition to carbon, most organic compounds contain hydrogen, many contain oxygen, nitrogen, or the halogens, and the elements sulfur and phosphorus occur fairly commonly. Significantly, all these elements lie in the upper right-hand corner of the periodic table. Other elements occur only infrequently in organic compounds. Historically, as more and more organic compounds were isolated and analyzed, by methods described in Chapter

---

[1] E. Griswold, *Chemical Bonding and Structure*, D. C. Heath and Co., Boston, 1967.

4

4, it was soon discovered that compounds representing many simple molecular formulas could be prepared, but, in spite of repeated attempts, others could not. For example, among those compounds composed solely of carbon and hydrogen, only one compound was found which contained a single carbon atom, CH_4. Three, and only three, compounds could be found which contained two carbon atoms, namely C_2H_2, C_2H_4 and C_2H_6. An understanding of the structure of organic compounds must begin by accounting for both the existence of these compounds and the inability to find others, such as CH_2, CH_3, C_2H_8, and so on.

STRUCTURAL THEORY OF ORGANIC CHEMISTRY

During the period from 1830–1860, a set of ideas gradually developed into a structural theory of organic chemistry. The utility of this theory arose from the fact that the existence, or nonexistence, of a compound with a particular molecular formula could be accurately predicted on the basis of the following assumptions:

1. Each carbon atom has four, and only four, valences. Similarly, each nitrogen has three valences, each oxygen has two, while hydrogen and the halogens each have just one. A stable compound will be formed whenever each atom present has all of its valences "satisfied"—i.e., attached to other atoms.

2. A carbon atom may be joined to another atom by either one, two, or three of its valences. The same is true of nitrogen, while oxygen may be joined by either one or two valences.

3. The four valences of a carbon atom are directed towards the corners of a regular tetrahedron, with angles of 109.5° between each pair.

On this basis, the compounds C_2H_2, C_2H_4, and C_2H_6 were formulated as involving a "triple bond," a "double bond," and a "single bond" joining the two carbon atoms, respectively, the term *bond* signifying the joining of the valences of two atoms and being represented by a straight line joining the atoms as in the following formulas:

$$H-C\equiv C-H \qquad \begin{matrix} H & & H \\ & \diagdown & \diagup & \\ & C & = & C \\ & \diagup & & \diagdown \\ H & & H \end{matrix} \qquad \begin{matrix} H & H \\ | & | \\ H-C-C-H \\ | & | \\ H & H \end{matrix}$$

Acetylene   Ethylene   Ethane

Although they have been refined and extended in the intervening century, the basic concepts of this structural theory continue to guide the thinking of organic chemists.

THE COVALENT BOND

During the first quarter of the 20th century the development of a theory of electronic structure of the atom led to the concept of the covalent bond, in which two atoms are thought of as being held together by the mutual attraction of their nuclei for a pair of electrons located between them. It is useful to consider the covalent bond as resulting from the *overlap* of two atomic orbitals, one from each of the atoms involved, to form the region between the nuclei where the pair of bonding electrons resides. If each atom contributes one of the two bonding electrons, the number of covalent bonds which an atom can form is equal to the number of half-filled atomic orbitals which the atom possesses. It is this concept which relates the mysterious "valences" of structural theory to modern electronic theory. Hydrogen, for example, with the electronic configuration $1s^1$, has a single atomic orbital containing one electron and can form only one covalent bond; that is, hydrogen has only a "valence" of one. Precisely the same statement can be made of fluorine, with the electronic structure $1s^2 2s^2 2p_x^2 2p_y^2 2p_z^1$. Similar reasoning predicts the formation of two covalent bonds to an oxygen atom and three to a nitrogen atom. Only in the case of the carbon atom is it necessary to assume that the atom is in an excited electronic state, namely $1s^2 2s^1 2p_x^1 2p_y^1 2p_z^1$, in order to account for the formation of four covalent bonds.

It should be noted that it is also possible to propose the formation of a covalent bond in which both bonding electrons come from an atomic orbital on one of the atoms. Of the five electrons in the outer shell of the nitrogen atom in ammonia, NH_3, three are involved in the bonds to hydrogen, and the remaining two occupy an atomic orbital on nitrogen which is not involved in bonding. The basicity of ammonia results from the overlap of this latter *filled* orbital with the *empty* atomic orbital of a hydrogen ion, H^+, to form the ammonium ion, NH_4^+.

$$
\begin{array}{ccc}
\text{H} & & \text{H} \\
| & & |+ \\
\text{H}-\text{N}: & +\ H^+ \longrightarrow & \text{H}-\text{N}-\text{H} \\
| & & | \\
\text{H} & & \text{H}
\end{array}
$$

Bonds which result from the overlap of the lone pair of electrons in a filled orbital with the empty orbital of another atom, often termed *coordinate-covalent bonds*, are of great importance in the interpretation of the chemistry of many organic compounds, particularly those containing nitrogen or oxygen.

MOLECULAR GEOMETRY

Molecules not only exist in a variety of compositions but in a variety of shapes and sizes as well. Figure 2–1 shows the approximate

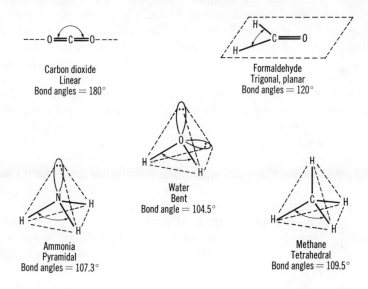

Carbon dioxide
Linear
Bond angles = 180°

Formaldehyde
Trigonal, planar
Bond angles = 120°

Water
Bent
Bond angle = 104.5°

Ammonia
Pyramidal
Bond angles = 107.3°

Methane
Tetrahedral
Bond angles = 109.5°

Figure 2–1 Some simple compounds illustrating the most common molecular shapes.

molecular shapes for several simple compounds, along with the description of the geometry of the compound and the approximate bond angles involved. (Bond angle refers to the angle formed by two lines joining the nucleus of a central atom to the nuclei of two adjacent atoms.) Nearly all organic compounds are composed of atoms whose geometrical arrangement and bond angles closely approximate one of the five shapes described in Figure 2–1.

There is a close correspondence between the bond angles at a particular atom and the total number of atoms and unshared pairs of electrons to which it is attached. In three of the compounds shown in Figure 2–1, the central atom is attached to a total of four such groups and unshared pairs:

methane—carbon is attached to four hydrogen atoms
ammonia—nitrogen is attached to three hydrogens and an electron pair
water—oxygen is attached to two hydrogens and two electron pairs.

In each case the bond angles about the central atom of each of these compounds are close to those expected from an arrangement in which each of the four attached groups occupies one corner of a tetrahedron. The carbon atom in formaldehyde, however, is attached to only three atoms and has no unshared electron pairs. There is a corresponding change in geometry, to a flat molecule with bond angles close to those which would be expected if the attached groups were positioned at the corners of an equilateral triangle (120°) with the central carbon atom at the center. Similarly, the carbon atom in carbon dioxide, attached to two atoms and with no unshared electrons, exhibits a still different geometry, its bond angle of 180° resulting in a linear molecule. These observations can be summarized in a useful generalization known as the principle of maximum separation of orbitals: "All of the atoms *and* unshared electron pairs attached to a particular atom tend to be distributed in space in such a manner as to be separated as far from one another as possible." With rare exceptions, predictions of the geometry of organic compounds made on the basis of this principle come within a few degrees of the experimentally determined bond angles. An extensive discussion of molecular geometry and its effects is contained in reference (2).

HYBRIDIZATION OF ATOMIC ORBITALS

If the covalent bond is a result of the overlap of atomic orbitals, then there must be atomic orbitals which form angles of 109.5°, 120°, and 180° with one another, in order to account for these observed bond angles. Of the simple atomic orbitals which might be involved, the $2s$ is spherical in shape and therefore nondirectional, and the three "propeller-shaped" $2p$ orbitals are oriented at angles of 90° to one another. It is important to note, however, that the mathematical

---

(2) W. Herz, *The Shape of Carbon Compounds*, W. A. Benjamin, Inc., New York, 1963.

functions which describe these particular orbitals are only four out of an infinite set of functions which satisfy the conditions of the wave equation for a principal quantum number of two. More specifically, any linear combination of the functions describing the $2s$ and $2p$ orbitals describes a new orbital with a principal quantum number of two. Termed a "hybrid" orbital, this new orbital, although higher in energy than those from which it was formed, will also have a different shape and geometrical relationship to the other atomic orbitals. In favorable cases, the hybrid orbital, because of its shape, forms a much stronger covalent bond than the simple atomic orbitals, and the stability of this bond more than compensates for the higher energy of the orbital itself. Of particular interest are those hybrid orbitals in which two or more simple atomic orbitals are combined to form an equal number of *equivalent* orbitals. Thus, the $2s$ and $2p_x$ orbitals can be combined to form two orbitals of identical shape and energy (called sp orbitals from the symbols for the component orbitals). Each of the sp orbitals is directed along the x axis, but in opposite directions (180° apart), and each is oriented at 90° to the unhybridized p_y and p_z orbitals. Table 2–1 summarizes the three common types of hybridization found in elements of the second period (Li-Ne) and the associated geometrical distribution of these orbitals. It cannot be emphasized too strongly that there is a one-to-one correspondence between the directional properties of these hybrid orbitals and the shapes of molecules, as observed experimentally or as predicted on the basis of the principle of maximum separation of orbitals.

Table 2–1

Some Properties of Hybrid Orbitals of the Second Period Elements

Hybrid Designation	No. of Hybrid Orbitals	Atomic orbitals used in Hybrids	Atomic orbitals Remaining Unhybridized	Angle between Hybrid Orbitals	Angle between Hybrid and Unhybridized Orbitals
sp	2	$2s, 2p_x$	$2p_y, 2p_z$	180°	90°
sp^2	3	$2s, 2p_x, 2p_y$	$2p_z$	120°	90°
sp^3	4	$2s, 2p_x, 2p_y, 2p_z$	—	109.5°	—

NATURE OF DOUBLE BONDS: SIGMA AND PI BONDS

Referring again to the compounds illustrated in Figure 2–1, the fact that formaldehyde (I) is found to be a trigonal, planar compound leads immediately to the expectation that the orbitals employed by carbon in its bonds to hydrogen and oxygen are sp^2 hybrid orbitals. Each of these bonds is described as a "sigma" bond, or σ-bond, indicating that the electron pair which constitutes each bond is concentrated along a line joining the two nuclei (heavy black lines in structure II). A glance at the conventional electronic formula for formaldehyde (I) reveals the presence of a second pair of electrons in the bond between carbon and oxygen. This bond must somehow involve the fourth orbital of carbon, not accounted for in the set of sp^2 orbitals, which (cf. Table 2–1) is a $2p$ orbital perpendicular to the plane of the hybrid orbitals. The "other half" of the double bond is then pictured as a "sideways" overlap of this $2p$ orbital on carbon with a similar $2p$ orbital on oxygen as shown by the double arrows in

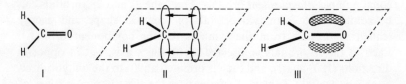

I   II   III

II. Since these orbitals overlap above and below the plane formed by the four nuclei, the electron pair in this bond is pictured as being concentrated in two banana-shaped regions, one above and one below the σ-bond, as shown by the cross-hatched regions in III. The term "pi" bond, or π-bond, is used to describe this type of bond and distinguish it from the more conventional σ-bond. In general, then, what is written as a double bond consists of two basically different types of bonding arrangements, a σ-bond, which is equivalent to a single covalent bond, and a π-bond in which the electron pair "brackets" the σ-bond. (For a description of an alternative model for bonding in double bonds, reference (3) may be consulted.)

BOND POLARITY

The covalent bond in the hydrogen molecule and similar structures is symmetrical, with the electron pair being attracted equally by the two identical nuclei. Whenever a covalent bond is formed between nonidentical atoms, however, the electron pair will likely be attracted more by one nucleus than by the other. Again using formaldehyde as an example, the electrons in the double bond are more strongly

---

[3] E. A. Walters, *J. Chem. Educ.*, **43**, 134 (1966).

attracted to the oxygen nucleus than to the carbon, and consequently they tend to be concentrated toward the oxygen end of the bond. The result is the accumulation of negative charge at the oxygen end of the bond and a corresponding accumulation of positive charge at the carbon. Consequently, such a bond is described as *polar*. Some of the effects of polar bonds upon physical and chemical properties will be discussed in Chapters 3 and 5, respectively.

Predictions of bond polarity are made on the basis of the relative electronegativities of the two elements between which the bond is formed. Several semi-quantitative scales of electronegativity have been proposed, and some selected values are shown in Table 2–2. The higher the electronegativity of the element, the greater the attraction for a pair of bonding electrons, and, in general, the greater the difference between the electronegativity values for two elements, the more polar will be a bond between the elements. As an example, consider the compounds CH_4, NH_3, and H_2O. Since the electronegativity values for carbon and hydrogen are so similar, the C—H bond is nearly nonpolar. Both nitrogen and oxygen are more electronegative than hydrogen, and the N—H and O—H bonds are both polarized in the same direction, hydrogen being the electron-poor or positive end in each case. The greater difference between the electronegativities of oxygen (3.5) and hydrogen (2.1) than between nitrogen (3.0) and hydrogen (2.1) leads to the prediction that the O—H bond will be considerably more polar than the N—H bond.

Table 2–2

Electronegativity Values for Some Common Elements

H 2.1	Si 1.8	F 4.0
C 2.5	P 2.1	Cl 3.0
N 3.0	S 2.5	Br 2.8
O 3.5		I 2.5

HYDROCARBON CHAINS, ALKANES AND THE UNIQUENESS OF CARBON

Having thus briefly reviewed the basic principles of the covalent bond, it is now time to turn to an explicit consideration of the nature of organic compounds. Whereas most pairs of elements form only a handful of different binary compounds, the binary compounds of carbon and hydrogen, known collectively as hydrocarbons, number well over five thousand!

An understanding of this vast array of compounds begins with the relationship between the two simplest hydrocarbons, methane (IV) and ethane (V), C_2H_6. (The reader is reminded that formulas IV–VII are planar representations of the three-dimensional structure of these compounds, in which the four bonds of each carbon atom are directed towards the corners of a tetrahedron. The use of molecular models to help visualize the shapes of molecules is recommended.) From the standpoint of bonding, the only difference between methane (IV) and

<pre>
      H   H H   H H H
      | | | | | |
  H—C—H   H—C—C—H   H—C—C—C—H
      | | | | | |
      H   H H   H H H
     IV   V   VI
</pre>

<pre>
          H H H H
          | | | |
      H—C—C—C—C—H
          | | | |
          H H H H
               VII
</pre>

ethane (V) is that, in the latter compound, one of the sp^3 hybrid orbitals on each carbon atom overlaps with an orbital of the other carbon atom rather than with a hydrogen atom. Similarly, there is a third compound, propane (VI), with the formula C_3H_8, which bears the same relationship to ethane that ethane does to methane. The series continues through butane (VII), C_4H_{10}, to pentane, C_5H_{12}, and so on, each compound differing from the preceding by the addition of a CH_2 unit. In principle, there is virtually no limit to the number of analogous compounds which could be formed, each with the formula C_nH_{2n+2}, and each consisting of a chain of n carbon atoms connected by single bonds with the remainder of the four bonds of each carbon being attached to hydrogen atoms. In fact, the largest such compound to have been isolated in pure form at the present time is $C_{110}H_{222}$! This family of compounds, known as alkanes, is but one of several families of hydrocarbons.

The formation of such an extensive series of binary compounds between carbon and hydrogen is not, in itself, difficult to understand. But why, one may ask, do not other elements combine with hydrogen to form similar series of compounds? Such behavior might certainly be expected from the nearest neighbors of carbon, namely boron, nitrogen, and silicon. If nitrogen were to form a series of compounds analogous to the alkanes, they would have the molecular formulas: NH_3, N_2H_4, N_3H_5, N_4H_6, and so on. In fact, only the first two members of this series, NH_3 and N_2H_4, are known. Very abbreviated series of binary compounds with hydrogen are also known for boron and silicon. Only carbon forms an extensive array. This difference can be accounted for in terms of two properties, stability and reactivity, in which the alkanes differ significantly from the analogous compounds of the elements boron, nitrogen, and silicon. Stability, as used above, is an ambiguous term, but one way of considering stability is in terms of the strengths of the covalent bonds involved in the molecule. Both the C—H and C—C bonds are moderately strong, i.e., difficult to break, and for this reason, CH_4, C_2H_6 and the higher alkanes are of comparable stability. With nitrogen, however, although the N—H bond is of similar strength to the C—H, the N—N bond is *very* weak in comparison. Thus, NH_3 is quite a stable compound, but N_2H_4 (hydrazine) is relatively unstable due to the presence of the N—N bond (it is used as a rocket fuel, in fact), and the higher homologs, which would have more than one N—N bond, are unknown. A similar situation exists in the case of silicon. Unreactivity, which is the most characteristic chemical property of the alkanes, results not only from the presence of relatively strong nonpolar bonds, but also from the lack of sensitive sites which can be readily approached by attacking reagents. It will be shown in Chapter 5 that most organic reactions occur at sites which possess a polar bond, or which possess either a vacant orbital or an unshared pair of electrons. The alkanes obviously possess none of these structural features and their lack of reactivity is thus to be expected. In contrast, ammonia and its relatives have an unshared electron pair on each nitrogen atom as well as the relatively polar N—H bonds, both of which contribute to the reactivity of ammonia. The situation with the silicon compounds, SiH_4, Si_2H_6, ..., is more subtle, for like the alkanes they possess no polar bonds or unshared electron pairs. The critical difference in reactivity between silicon and carbon compounds results from the orbitals used in bond formation. The fact that silicon uses hybridized $3s$ and $3p$ orbitals in bond formation, rather than $2s$ and $2p$, allows the vacant $3d$ orbitals on silicon to serve as points of attack for many reagents. In the case of carbon, the $3d$ orbitals are too high in energy to allow their use. To summarize, carbon is indeed unique in its ability, with the cooperation of hydrogen, to form extensive chains. The unreactivity of these chains depends upon the fact that all of the orbitals of carbon are involved in fairly strong, nonpolar bonds.

OTHER HYDROCARBON FAMILIES: ALKENES, ALKYNES, CYCLOALKANES

In the alkanes, all of the bonds between carbon atoms are single covalent bonds. It is possible, also, of course, for carbon atoms to be joined by a double bond, and the inclusion of a double bond in a hydrocarbon chain leads to a new family of compounds known as alkenes. The first three members of this series, whose structures are shown in VIII–X, are known as ethylene (C_2H_4), propylene (C_3H_6), and 1-butene (C_4H_8), respectively. As with the alkanes, the number of possible alkenes is virtually unlimited, as the length of the chain can,

$$\overset{H}{\underset{H}{}} C = C \overset{H}{\underset{H}{}}$$

VIII

IX

X

in theory, be extended indefinitely. Alkenes obviously contain two hydrogen atoms less than the corresponding alkanes and can be assigned the general formula C_nH_{2n}. The alkene double bond, like the carbon–oxygen double bond described earlier (cf. I–III), consists of a σ-bond and a π-bond, as shown in XI. The two participating carbon atoms and the four hydrogen atoms to which they are attached all lie in the same plane, and they are "frozen" in this configuration by the π-bond, which prevents rotation of one end of the molecule relative to the other.

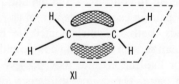

XI

Because of the diminished hydrogen content of alkenes, they are often referred to as "unsaturated" hydrocarbons, the double bond itself often being described as a source of unsaturation. A second family of unsaturated hydrocarbons, the alkynes, contains a triple bond between two of the carbon atoms in the chain, the resulting general formula being C_nH_{2n-2}. Acetylene (XII), C_2H_2, is the simplest alkyne and is familiar as a fuel used for welding. The next higher homologs, propyne (C_3H_4) and 1-butyne (C_4H_6), are shown in XIII and XIV, respectively. Compounds containing more than one carbon–

14

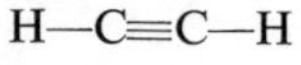

H—C≡C—H   H—C—C≡C—H   H—C—C—C≡C—H

(with H atoms as drawn)

XII 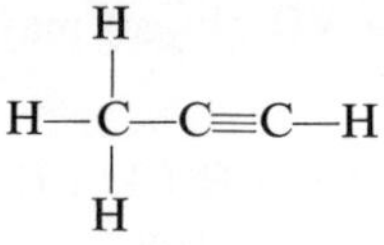   XIII 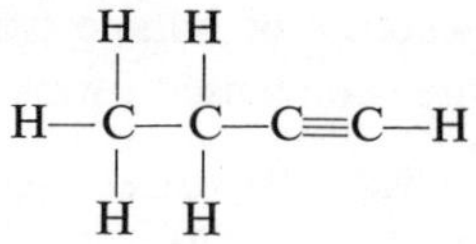   XIV

carbon double or triple bond constitute additional, less common families of unsaturated hydrocarbons.

The possibility of joining the two end carbons of an alkane chain to form a cyclic structure, or ring, constitutes another interesting structural variation. The resulting family of compounds, known as cycloalkanes (XV–XVIII), has the general formula C_nH_{2n}. Cycloalkanes

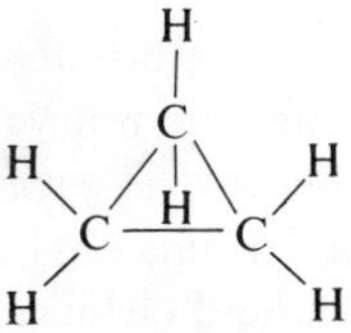

XV 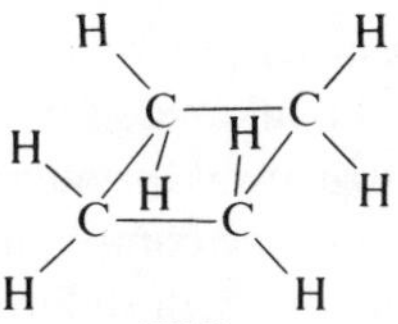   XVI

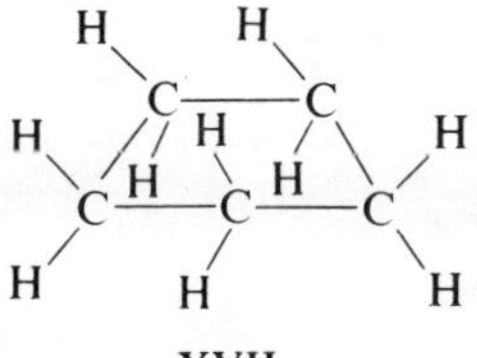

XVII 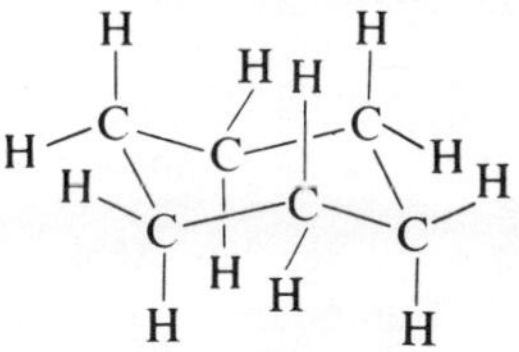   XVIII

as large as $C_{54}H_{108}$ have been prepared, but it is still the chemistry of the 5- and 6-membered rings which attracts the greatest attention, at least partly due to the common occurrence of these rings in compounds of biological interest.

CONDENSED FORMULAS

Although structural formulas of the type we have used thus far convey an adequate picture of the structure of a molecule, they become very cumbersome as the structure becomes more complex. Thus, it is common to use an abbreviated or condensed method of writing formulas in which a carbon atom and its associated hydrogen atoms are grouped together as a unit. The terminal carbon of an alkane chain, for example, with three hydrogens attached, is written as —CH_3. Bonds between carbon atoms may be indicated by lines, as previously, or these may also be omitted if no ambiguity results. The structure of butane (structure VII above) may be written in at least three condensed forms:

CH$_3$—CH$_2$—CH$_2$—CH$_3$ CH$_3$CH$_2$CH$_2$CH$_3$ CH$_3$(CH$_2$)$_2$CH$_3$
            (a)   (b)   (c)

The last representation (c) groups together two identical groups (CH$_2$) which occur consecutively. In "translating" condensed formulas, the reader need keep in mind only the requirement of four bonds to carbon and confusion will be avoided.

ISOMERISM

Having looked at the basic features of hydrocarbons, we return now to take a second look at the alkanes, for even that story is not yet complete. On page 12 the structural formula for the alkane C$_4$H$_{10}$ was described. Yet there is not just one compound with the formula C$_4$H$_{10}$ but two, butane and isobutane, with different physical and chemical properties (Table 2–3). This is but one of innumerable examples of the

Table 2–3

Some Properties of Butane and Isobutane

Compound	Molecular Formula	Melting Point, °C	Boiling Point, °C	Density g/ml ($-20°$)
Butane	C$_4$H$_{10}$	-135.0	-0.5	0.622
Isobutane	C$_4$H$_{10}$	-159	-12	0.604

existence of different compounds with the same molecular formula. Such compounds are called *isomers*, indicating that they are composed of the same atoms (Greek: *iso*, same + *meros*, part). The fact that we have identified only one structure corresponding to C$_4$H$_{10}$ is clearly evidence that the structural theory which has been presented is not complete. The omission results from the implicit assumption that the carbon atoms in an alkane are arranged in a straight chain, as in XIX, when they might just as well have been arranged in branched, or T, fashion, as in XX. Since these are the only two acceptable formulas

XIX   XX

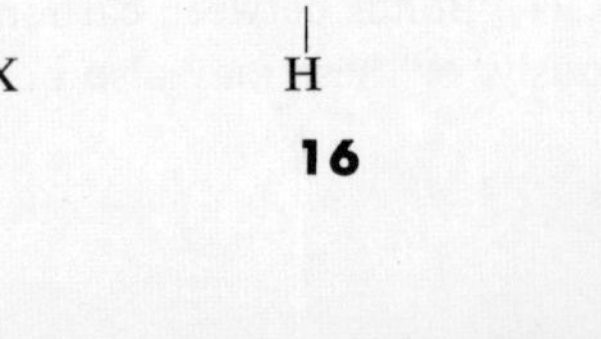

which can be written for C_4H_{10}, they may be assumed to represent the two known isomers of C_4H_{10}. Which of the compounds in Table 2–3 corresponds to XIX and which to XX is a problem in structure determination (Chapter 4), the results of which indicate that XIX represents butane and XX isobutane.

The two isomers of butane contain the same number (3) of C—C bonds and C—H bonds (10) but they differ in the arrangement of the carbon atoms in the backbone of the chain. They are termed *skeletal* isomers. At this point, it will be useful to describe other types of isomerism, drawing examples from the families of compounds already discussed.

Position isomers—Example: 1-butene (XXI) and 2-butene (XXII)—contain the same number and types of bonds, and the same carbon skeleton, but differ in the point on the chain where some type of substitution occurs (in this example, the double bond constitutes the substitution).

$$CH_3—CH_2—CH{=}CH_2 \qquad CH_3—CH{=}CH—CH_3 \qquad \begin{matrix} CH_2—CH_2 \\ |\qquad\ | \\ CH_2—CH_2 \end{matrix}$$

| XXI | XXII | XXIII |

Functional isomers—Example: 1-butene (XXI) and cyclobutane (XXIII)—differ in the types of bonds; i.e., 1-butene contains two carbon–carbon single bonds and a double bond, while cyclobutane contains four single carbon–carbon bonds.

Stereoisomers contain the same types of bonds, the same skeletal arrangement, and the positions of any substitutions on the chain are identical; they differ only in the shape of the molecule, or, in other words, in the spatial relationship between the atoms in the molecule. One type of stereoisomerism, known as *geometrical isomerism*, occurs in alkenes such as 2-butene (XXII). Here the planarity of the molecule (cf. XI) results in the possibility of two distinctly different structures, one in which the two central hydrogen atoms are on the same side of the double bond (XXIV) and one in which they are on opposite sides (XXV). The comparison of properties in Table 2–4 shows that these two compounds, *cis*-2-butene (XXIV) and *trans*-2-butene (XXV), differ significantly in their physical behavior.

$$\begin{matrix} CH_3 & & CH_3 \\ & \diagdown\quad\diagup & \\ & C{=}C & \\ & \diagup\quad\diagdown & \\ H & & H \end{matrix} \qquad\qquad \begin{matrix} CH_3 & & H \\ & \diagdown\quad\diagup & \\ & C{=}C & \\ & \diagup\quad\diagdown & \\ H & & CH_3 \end{matrix}$$

| XXIV | XXV |

Table 2—4

Some Properties of cis- *and* trans-2-*Butene*

	Boiling Point, °C	Melting Point, °C	Heat of Fusion, kcal/mole	Density at 20°C, g/ml
cis-2-Butene (XXIV)	+3.7	−139	1.75	0.621
trans-2-Butene (XXV)	+0.9	−106	2.33	0.604

A more subtle type of stereoisomerism, known as optical isomerism, occurs in compounds such as 2-chlorobutane (XXVI-A) in which there are four *different* groups attached to a single carbon atom. When this structure is seen as a model or in perspective view, it is found that there are two distinctly different ways of distributing the four groups around the central carbon, as seen in XXVI-B and XXVI-C. Structure XXVI-C is a mirror image of XXVI-B, but no amount of twisting or

turning can make the two forms superimposable. (The relationship between XXVI-B and XXVI-C is the same as that between a right-handed and a left-handed glove.) Members of such a pair of mirror-image isomers have identical melting points, boiling points, densities, and other physical properties with one important exception. When plane polarized light passes through a sample of either isomer, the plane of the polarized light is rotated, one isomer rotating the plane in a clockwise direction and the other in a counterclockwise direction. It is this property which leads to the term *optical isomers*, and a substance which behaves in this manner is said to be optically active. If equal quantities of each member of a pair of optical isomers are mixed, the molecules of one isomer counteract the effect of the other isomer upon plane polarized light, so that the resulting mixture, termed a *racemic* mixture, has no effect.

FUNCTIONAL GROUPS—AN ORGANIZING PRINCIPLE

Since the alkane chain itself is so unreactive under most conditions, the introduction of a multiple bond or the replacement of one or more hydrogens on the chain by an atom of a different element usually leads to a molecule of greater reactivity. Furthermore, when reaction does occur, it will most likely occur at this new site. Ethyl chloride, for example, reacts with hydroxide ion to form ethyl alcohol, equation (2–1), under conditions where ethane itself is totally unreactive.

$$CH_3\!-\!CH_2\!-\!Cl + OH^- \rightarrow CH_3\!-\!CH_2\!-\!OH + Cl^- \qquad (2\text{–}1)$$

Since only the carbon–chlorine bond is affected by this reaction, it is at least approximately true that *any* chlorine atom attached to an alkane chain can be replaced by OH upon treatment with hydroxide ion. This fact is indicated by the general equation (2–2), in which the symbol R—Cl represents any compound in which a chlorine is attached to a carbon atom of a saturated hydrocarbon chain.

$$R\!-\!Cl + OH^- \rightarrow R\!-\!OH + Cl^- \qquad (2\text{–}2)$$

These compounds, then, constitute a family of compounds, known as alkyl chlorides, which exhibit similar chemical behavior based upon the presence of the chlorine. The organic chemist refers to the chlorine atom as a *functional group*, since it is the part of the alkyl chloride molecule which "functions" in the reactions of this family of compounds.

The chlorine atom is just one of a number of possible functional groups, and there is a different family of compounds corresponding to each functional group. The carbon–carbon double bond is a functional group, and, as we have seen, the family of compounds containing the double bond is known as the alkenes. Similarly, the functional group characteristic of the alkynes is the carbon–carbon triple bond. On the inside of the back cover, you will find a list of the names of the more common functional groups along with the structural formula for each and the name of the family of compounds in which it is found. In the succeeding chapters, this list should be consulted whenever the name of a family of compounds is mentioned, until these names can be immediately associated with the appropriate functional groups.

It should be re-emphasized at this point that the value of the functional group concept lies in the degree to which the properties, particularly the chemical properties, of any organic compound are similar to other members of the same family. It is thus possible to summarize the chemistry of most alkenes, for example, by describing the reactions of the carbon–carbon double bond and how these reactions may be affected by the structure of the alkene. Although not all of the functional groups which occur in organic compounds are shown inside the back cover, a thorough understanding of the reactions of even this small number of functional groups can account for the chemical behavior of a sizeable fraction of the million or so organic compounds.

NOMENCLATURE

If each new organic compound were named after its discoverer or the place at which it was first synthesized, as many of the elements have been, communication between organic chemists would be virtually impossible. The number of names for compounds would exceed the number of words in an unabridged dictionary by something like a factor of four! Thus it is not difficult to see the need for a *system of nomenclature*, one in which, on the basis of a set of simple rules, a name can be assigned to any compound. This name must be susceptible to correct interpretation by any chemist familiar with the system. A complete description of the systematic nomenclature formulated by the International Union of Pure and Applied Chemistry (IUPAC) is beyond the scope of this book. Some knowledge of the principles upon which it is based, however, will prove instructive.

In the IUPAC system, each functional group is assigned a suffix, some of which are shown in Table 2–5; others are included with the list of functional groups on the inside back cover. A quick glance, therefore, at the final segment of an IUPAC name serves to identify the family to which the compound belongs. Thus, the name of one of the common insect repellents, 2-ethyl-1,3-hexanediol, identifies the functional group in this substance as an —OH group. In fact, the "di," immediately preceding the suffix -ol signifies the presence of

Table 2—5

IUPAC Suffixes for Some Common Functional Groups

Structure	Family Name	IUPAC Suffix	Structure	Family Name	IUPAC Suffix
R—H	Alkane	-ane	$R-\overset{O}{\overset{\|}{C}}-H$	Aldehyde	-al
$R_2C{=}CR_2$	Alkene	-ene	$R-\overset{O}{\overset{\|}{C}}-R$	Ketone	-one
$RC{\equiv}CR$	Alkyne	-yne	R—COOH	Carboxylic Acid	-oic acid
R—OH	Alcohol	-ol			

not just one but two —OH groups. The parent name in the IUPAC system, to which the functional group suffix is appended, is the name of the longest *straight* alkane chain to which the functional group is attached. The names of the alkanes are, therefore, of particular importance, and they, in turn, are based upon often familiar terms indicating the number of carbon atoms which the alkane contains. The names of the alkanes having one to ten carbon atoms are shown inside the front cover for easy reference. In completing the IUPAC name, the carbon atoms of the parent alkane are numbered, starting at the end nearest the functional group, and the position of the functional group is indicated by referring to the number of the carbon atom to which it is attached. Finally, the names of any additional groups attached to the parent chain are included, along with numbers signifying the points of attachment, prior to the parent name.

Returning to the previous example, 2-ethyl-1,3-hexanediol, the parent name *hexane* indicates a straight chain of six carbon atoms. The numbers 1 and 3 identify the carbon atoms to which the two —OH groups are attached, and the first portion of the name, 2-ethyl, identifies the presence of an ethyl group attached to the second carbon atom of the hexane chain.

$$CH_3-CH_2-CH_2-\underset{\underset{CH_2CH_3}{|}}{\overset{\overset{OH}{|}}{CH}}-\overset{\overset{OH}{|}}{CH}-CH_2 = \text{2-ethyl-1,3-hexanediol}$$

The correlation between suffixes and functional groups is so convenient and familiar to chemists that it is often used in common, nonsystematic names as well. The hormonal substance, cortis*one*, for example, is a ketone, and the name cholester*ol* correctly implies that this important substance contains the —OH functional group.

For many simple compounds, a less systematic nomenclature is commonly used, in which the chain attached to the functional group is assigned a simple name followed by a name denoting the functionality. The names of these *alkyl* groups, containing from one to four carbon atoms, are shown inside the front cover. The following examples will serve to illustrate how these common names are employed:

$$CH_3-\overset{\overset{OH}{|}}{CH}-CH_3 \qquad CH_3-CH_3-\overset{\overset{Cl}{|}}{CH}-CH_3 \qquad CH_3-\overset{\overset{O}{||}}{C}-CH_2-CH_3$$

Isopropyl alcohol   *sec*-butyl chloride   Methyl ethyl ketone

This description of organic nomenclature has been much too brief to enable the reader to utilize this vocabulary for himself in anything more than a very rudimentary manner. Hopefully, however, he has gained some understanding of how it is possible to approach the formidable task of naming a million compounds in a systematic manner. Moreover, he should be aware of the important correlation between nomenclature and functional groups. A programmed text, such as (4) or (5), may prove useful to the student who wishes to acquire a working knowledge of organic nomenclature.

AROMATICITY—A STRUCTURAL PECULIARITY

The development of an acceptable structural theory of organic chemistry was hampered by the fact that there always seemed to be one group of compounds which simply did not fit. These compounds were referred to as *aromatic* compounds, in deference to their characteristically strong, and often pleasant, odors (oil of wintergreen and vanilla flavoring being two familiar examples). The simplest aromatic compound, benzene, was discovered early in the history of organic chemistry and proved to have the molecular formula C_6H_6. This formula, like those of other aromatic compounds, obviously corresponded to a highly unsaturated compound. The puzzling feature of the formula C_6H_6 arose from the observations that, in spite of this obvious unsaturation,

1. benzene is both more stable and much less reactive than other unsaturated compounds, such as the alkenes

2. when benzene does react, it characteristically undergoes a very different type of reaction (substitution) than the addition reactions observed with alkenes and alkynes (cf. Chapter 5).

Clearly, either benzene was not to be formulated as having double bonds, or else some explanation would need to be found for the very different behavior of double bonds in aromatic systems from those in alkenes.

---

[4] O. T. Benfey, *The Names and Structures of Organic Compounds*, John Wiley and Sons, Inc., New York, 1966.

[5] J. Traynham, *Organic Nomenclature: A Programmed Introduction*, Prentice-Hall, Inc., Englewood Cliffs, N.J., 1966.

KEKULÉ AND THE STRUCTURE OF BENZENE

In addition to the facts concerning the reactions of aromatic compounds, considerable information was soon accumulated concerning substituted benzenes, obtained by replacing one of the hydrogens of benzene by an alkyl group or some functional group. It was possible to obtain only one isomer of a monosubstituted benzene, such as C_6H_5Cl or $C_6H_5CH_3$. In disubstituted benzenes, three different isomers could be obtained, regardless of whether the two substituent groups were identical, as in $C_6H_4Cl_2$, or different, as in $C_6H_4ClCH_3$. The small number of isomers obtainable indicated a highly symmetrical structure for benzene, and this was a helpful guide in searching for a structural interpretation of aromatic compounds.

The benzene structure proposed by August Kekulé a little over a century ago, as a result of his now legendary dream of a snake biting its own tail, was that of a ring of six carbon atoms, connected by alternate single and double bonds, with one hydrogen attached to each carbon (XXVII-A). The novelty in Kekulé's suggestion lay in his

XXVII-A   XXVII-B

further proposal that the position of the double bonds was constantly in a state of flux, "flipping" back and forth between position XXVII-A and XXVII-B. It was reasoned that they thus ceased to be typical double bonds, and consequently one might expect different chemical behavior from this aromatic ring. This structure neatly solved the isomer problem, for there is just one possible monosubstitution product of XXVII, and there are three disubstitution products possible, shown in structures XXVIII–XXX for the dichloro-derivatives, provided that the double bonds are constantly "flipping." Although Kekulé had succeeded in suggesting a structure which was consistent with the properties of aromatic compounds, he had little basis for his proposition of "flipping" double bonds, and a more acceptable explanation came only with the advent of modern bonding theory.

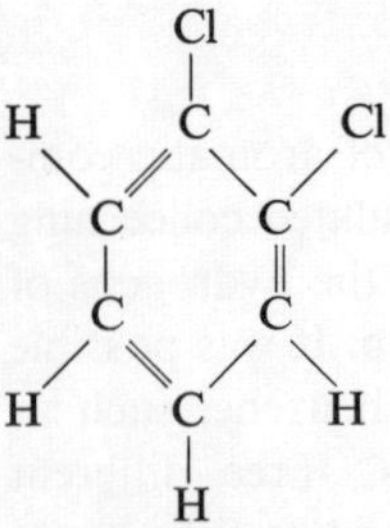

Cl
H   C   Cl
 C   C
 C   C
H   C   H
    H
XXVIII

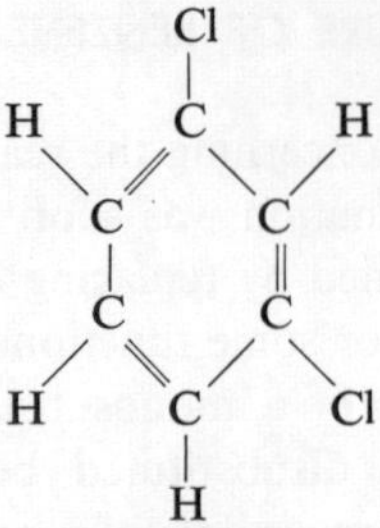

Cl
H   C   H
 C   C
 C   C
H   C   Cl
    H
XXIX

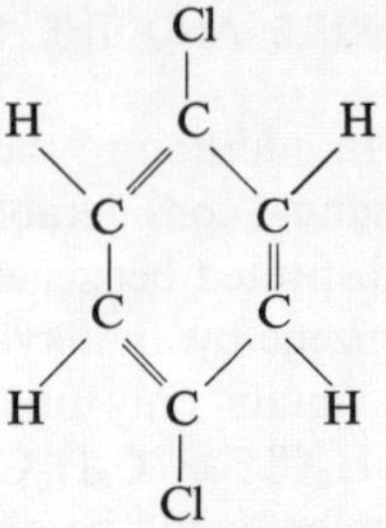

Cl
H   C   H
 C   C
 C   C
H   C   H
    Cl
XXX

BENZENE—A CONTEMPORARY PICTURE

More recent physical evidence has shown that the benzene molecule is indeed a flat, regular hexagon as suggested by Kekulé. There is no difference between the six carbon–carbon bonds in a benzene ring and they are intermediate in length between typical double and single bonds. To account for this structure theoretically, we return to the account of a double bond (p. 10), in which the two carbon atoms form a σ-bond by overlap of sp^2 orbitals and a π-bond by "sideways" overlap of a $2p$ atomic orbital from each carbon. The framework of benzene is similarly pictured as resulting from six sp^2 hybridized carbon atoms in a σ-bonded, planar hexagon (XXXI). The remaining p orbital of each carbon atom is directed perpendicularly to the plane

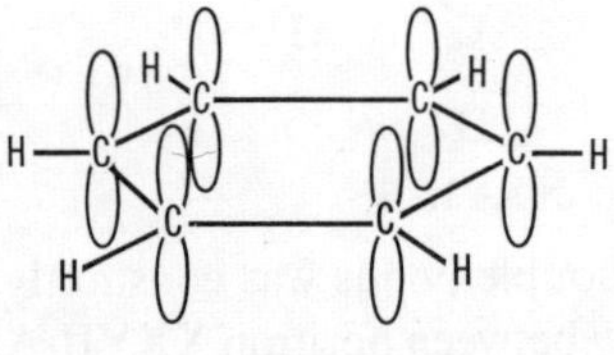

XXXI

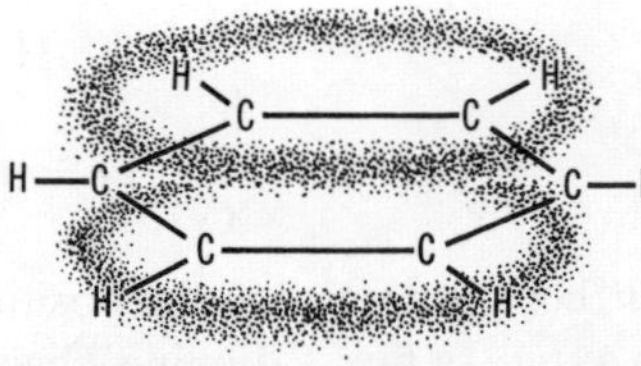

XXXII

of the six-membered ring. Now instead of the orbitals overlapping in pairs, as was proposed for the double bond, all six p orbitals merge to form "doughnut-shaped" orbitals above and below the plane of the ring (XXXII). The six electrons in these orbitals all move quite freely through these circular, π-orbitals. Since the energy of an electron is lowered by increasing the volume within which it is confined, it is the "delocalization" of these six π-electrons into a larger volume which results in the greatly enhanced stability of the benzene ring as compared with the alkenes. The lowered reactivity of aromatic rings is related not only to their stability, but also to the fact that the reactive

24

π-electrons are less concentrated in any one spot, and therefore more difficult for an attacking reagent to "grab."

Since representation of the benzene ring by one of the Kekulé forms can be misleading, due to the inclusion of double bonds, the symbol below is becoming increasingly common as a representation of the aromatic ring in benzene. It is assumed that at each vertex of the hexagon there is a carbon atom, and that attached to that carbon atom is a hydrogen atom, unless a different group is indicated.

DERIVATIVES OF BENZENE

Each of the functional groups listed inside the back cover may be attached to an aromatic ring, in place of one of the hydrogens, just as they may be attached to an alkane chain. A few typical compounds of this type are shown in XXXIII–XXXVI. The benzene ring in these compounds may be viewed both as a functional group and, in other contexts, as the hydrocarbon to which the functional group is attached. Benzoic acid (XXXV), for example, exhibits the typical properties of the carboxyl group, —COOH, but under different conditions the aromatic ring itself participates in reactions which are completely foreign to nonaromatic compounds. In most instances, the

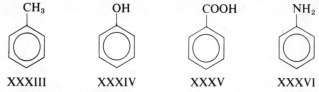

behavior of these simple benzene derivatives can be considered to reflect simply a combination of the properties of the benzene ring and the other functional group. This is true for both toluene (XXXIII) and benzoic acid (XXXV), and it is thus not necessary to consider them as members of special classes of compounds. There are, however, two common functional groups, —OH and —NH$_2$, which assume quite different properties when attached to an aromatic ring. Consequently, they are usually considered to form distinct classes of compounds, of which the parent members are phenol (XXXIV) and aniline (XXXVI).

As mentioned previously, when two of the hydrogens of benzene are replaced by other groups there are three possible position isomers. These isomers are distinguished from one another by the use of the prefixes *ortho-*, *meta-*, and *para-*, to designate adjacent carbons (XXXVII), alternate carbons (XXXVIII) and carbons on opposite sides of the ring (XXXIX), respectively. In writing the name of a compound, these prefixes are often abbreviated with the letters *o-*, *m-*, and *p-*. Thus, the compound *para*-dichlorobenzene, or *p*-dichloro-benzene, familiar as the active ingredient in mothballs, has the structure XXX.

ortho	*meta*	*para*
XXXVII	XXXVIII	XXXIX

OTHER AROMATIC SYSTEMS

Benzene is not the only ring system which exhibits the exceptional stability and the susceptibility to substitution reactions which characterize aromatic compounds. Most closely related to benzene are "condensed ring" aromatic systems, in which two six-membered rings share two adjacent carbon atoms, as in the three-ring molecule of phenanthrene (XXXX). It is thought that many condensed-ring aromatic hydrocarbons are carcinogenic, i.e., their presence may

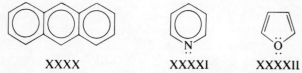

XXXX	XXXXI	XXXXII

induce the growth of cancerous tissue. Pyridine (XXXXI) and furan (XXXXII) represent an additional type of aromatic molecule. Known collectively as heterocyclic compounds, these structures in which one or more carbon atoms is replaced by an atom of another element are particularly important in biological systems.

The ability of the electronic theory of molecular structure to account for aromatic properties is discussed further in Chapter 6 and in reference (6), a very readable introduction to aromaticity.

---

[6] R. Breslow, *Chemical and Engineering News*, June 28, 1965, p. 90.

CHAPTER **3**

The Relationship Between
Physical Properties and Structure

Of the many physical properties which can be determined for any particular compound, of most immediate interest are those which can be utilized in one or more of the following ways:

1. rapid characterization of the compound, distinguishing it from other, similar substances;
2. separation of the compound from mixtures with other substances;
3. understanding, or even prediction and determination, of the structure and chemical behavior of the compound.

In this chapter, several common properties are discussed to show how and why they vary as they do with changes in the structure of the molecule.

BOILING POINTS

The *boiling point* (or, more properly, the *normal boiling point*) of a liquid is defined as the temperature at which the liquid exerts a vapor pressure of one atmosphere, or 760 Torr. Since intermolecular interactions are very important in the liquid state but nearly negligible in the vapor at one atmosphere pressure, the temperature at which a compound boils serves as a crude index of the strength of the intermolecular forces in the liquid. These intermolecular forces are principally of two types: dipole–dipole interactions and dispersion, or London, forces. The former occur only in polar molecules, resulting from the tendency of dipoles to line up so that the charges are attractive, as in Figure 3–1(a). Dispersion forces occur between any

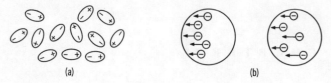

(a)   (b)

Figure 3–1 Representations of intermolecular forces resulting from (a) permanent dipoles and (b) momentary shifts in electron distributions.

two molecules, and result from a momentary shift in electron distribution in one of the molecules, inducing a similar imbalance in the electron distribution of the neighboring molecule, as in Figure 3–1(b). Although electron motion rapidly restores a symmetrical charge distribution, the effect of the momentary fluctuation is a net attraction between the two molecules. The magnitude of dispersion forces decreases very rapidly with increased distance between the molecules, but it will increase with an increase in the number of electrons in the molecule and with increased polarizability, i.e., the ease with which the electrons can be shifted around within the molecule. The origin of intermolecular forces is described more completely in reference (1).

The most familiar effect of structure upon boiling point is an increase in boiling point with increased molecular weight within a group of similar compounds. In Figure 3–2, the points on the solid line represent the boiling points of the straight chain alkanes with 3 to 10 carbon atoms, plotted as a function of the number of carbon atoms in the chain. The steady rise in boiling point shown by both this curve and those for the branched alkanes clearly demonstrates this effect of molecular weight. The higher temperatures required for the heavier compounds reflect greater intermolecular attractions between the heavier molecules. The greater attraction can be attributed to stronger dispersion forces resulting from the greater number of electrons in the molecules containing a greater number of carbon atoms. Because of their larger surface area, the heavier molecules also have more points of contact with other molecules and consequently experience a greater cumulative attraction to other molecules in the liquid state.

---

[1] B. V. Derjagin, *Scientific American*, July, 1960.

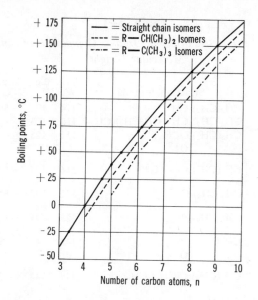

Figure 3–2 Boiling points of some alkanes, C_nH_{2n+2}, with 3–10 carbon atoms. ——— = straight chain isomers, – – – – = R—CH(CH$_3$)$_2$ isomers, —·— = R—C(CH$_3$)$_3$ isomers.

The effect of surface area can be seen even more clearly in the relative boiling points of the isomeric alkanes in Figure 3–2. As the 5-carbon alkanes, for example, become more branched, the surface area decreases and the boiling point does likewise, from 36° to 28° to 10°. Both the effect of increased molecular weight and that of chain branching are general phenomena, applicable to other classes of organic compounds as well as to the alkanes.

Something of the effect of functional groups upon boiling points can be gleaned from Table 3–1, in which some physical properties are listed for representatives of several classes of compounds, each compound having approximately the same molecular weight. Among the first ten compounds of Table 3–1 the differences in boiling points may be ascribed to expected differences in surface areas (cf. compounds 5 and 7) or polarity (cf. compounds 8 and 9). It is obvious that marked increases in boiling points occur in some of the last six compounds of Table 3–1, all of which may be considered to be derivatives of either water or ammonia. It is well known that water and ammonia exhibit unusually high boiling points for compounds of such low molecular weight, due to a remarkably strong type of dipole–dipole attraction

Table 3–1

Physical Properties of Some Organic Compounds of Similar Molecular Weight

Class of compound	Structural formula	Mol. Wt.	B.p., °C	M.p., °C	Sp. gr., 25°C
1. Alkane	$CH_3(CH_2)_6CH_3$	114	125	−56	0.70
2. Alkene	$CH_3(CH_2)_2CH=CH(CH_2)_2CH_3$	112	123	—	0.72
3. Ether	$CH_3(CH_2)_5OCH_3$	116	125	—	0.77
4. Ester	$CH_3(CH_2)_3\overset{O}{\overset{\|}{C}}OCH_3$	116	127	−91	0.89
5. Alkyl Chloride	$CH_3(CH_2)_5Cl$	121	132	−83	0.87
6. Alkyl Bromide	$CH_3(CH_2)_2Br$	123	71	−110	1.35
7. Alkyl Iodide	CH_3I	142	42	−94	2.28
8. Ketone	$CH_3(CH_2)_2\overset{O}{\overset{\|}{C}}(CH_2)_2CH_3$	114	144	−33	0.82
9. Aldehyde	$CH_3(CH_2)_5\overset{O}{\overset{\|}{C}}H$	114	155	−45	0.85
10. Amine (primary)	$CH_3(CH_2)_6NH_2$	115	158	−23	0.78
11. Amine (tertiary)	$CH_3(CH_2)_4N(CH_3)_2$	115	123	—	0.75
12. Alcohol	$CH_3(CH_2)_6OH$	116	176	−35	0.82
13. Carboxylic Acid	$CH_3(CH_2)_4\overset{O}{\overset{\|}{C}}OH$	116	205	−2	0.93
14. Carboxylic Acid	$CH_3\overset{O}{\overset{\|}{C}}OH$	60	118	+17	1.05
15. Amide	$CH_3(CH_2)_4\overset{O}{\overset{\|}{C}}NH_2$	115	255	+101	—

known as a *hydrogen bond*. Illustrated in Figure 3–3(a) for the compound methyl alcohol, the hydrogen bond is the result of electrostatic attraction between the negative charge on an electronegative atom, such as nitrogen or oxygen, and the "opposite side" of a hydrogen atom attached to such an electronegative atom. The hydrogen atom is peculiar in this respect, for when the electrons in a covalent bond to hydrogen are pulled strongly by the other atom, there are no inner electrons around the hydrogen nucleus to "screen" the positive charge of the nucleus. It is thus possible for the negative end of a neighboring molecule to move in quite close to the hydrogen, forming a strong

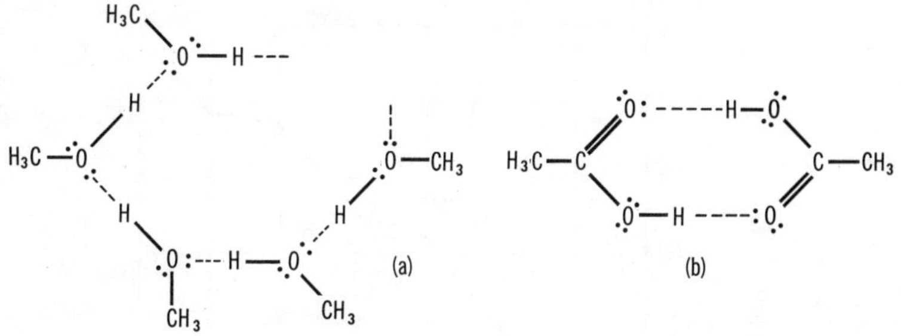

Figure 3-3 Hydrogen bonding between molecules of (a) methyl alcohol and (b) acetic acid. Dotted lines indicate hydrogen bonds.

attraction between the two opposite charges. As might be expected from a comparison of ammonia and water, hydrogen bonding appears to be weaker in amines (compound 10, Table 3-1) than in the corresponding alcohols (compound 12). It is also interesting to note that in the isomeric amine (compound 11) in which there is no longer an N—H available for hydrogen bonding, the boiling point drops to a value close to that of the alkane.

Among simple organic functional groups, the most strongly hydrogen bonded are those of the carboxylic acids (compounds 13 and 14) and amides (compound 15). The great strength of the hydrogen bonds in these compounds results from the simultaneous presence of a highly polar O—H or N—H bond, the carbon–oxygen double bond with its strong negative dipole toward the oxygen, and precisely the correct geometry for a very specific interaction between two molecules (Figure 3-3(b)). In fact, the hydrogen bonding between two molecules of acetic acid (compound 14 in Table 3-1) is so strong that the two-molecule unit shown in Figure 3-3(b) survives in the vapor phase as well as the liquid. It is thus not surprising that acetic acid boils at nearly the same temperature as many compounds with twice its molecular weight (see Table 3-1). The backbone of the giant biological molecules known as proteins (cf. Chapter 7) consists of a series of amide bonds, and the key to many of the properties of proteins lies in an understanding of the strong hydrogen bonds for which we see evidence here in boiling point data (see reference (2), for example).

(2) A. L. McClellan, *J. Chem. Educ.*, **44**, 547 (1967).

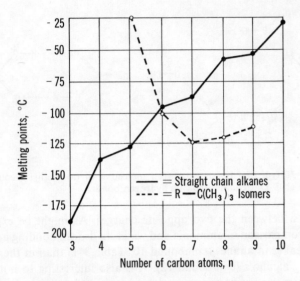

Figure 3–4 Melting points of some alkanes, C_nH_{2n+2}, with 3–10 carbon atoms. ———— = straight chain alkanes, – – – – = R—C(CH₃)₃ isomers.

MELTING POINTS

It is much more difficult to correlate the melting points of organic compounds with their structure than it is the boiling points. This is partly due to the fact that intermolecular distances are similar in liquid and solid phases, making intermolecular attractions also similar. Figure 3–4 shows that melting points within a family such as the straight chain alkanes also rise with increasing molecular weight, although not so regularly as the boiling points. The family of branched alkanes, however, is much more erratic in its melting behavior, the lower members of the series actually passing through a pronounced minimum at the stage of the 7 and 8 carbon compounds. These unusually high melting points for the smaller molecules are presumably due to their highly symmetrical structure, allowing a more compact "fit" into the crystal lattice. Another example of the effect of structural symmetry upon melting points is seen in Figure 3–5. Of the three isomeric dichlorobenzenes, the highly symmetrical *para*-isomer melts some 75° higher than the other two.

32

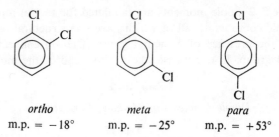

ortho | meta | para
m.p. = −18° | m.p. = −25° | m.p. = +53°

Figure 3-5 Structures and melting points of the three isomers of dichlorobenzene.

DIPOLE MOMENT

If a molecule is polar, i.e., if it possesses a positive end and a negative end, then when placed between the charged plates of an electrical condenser, the molecules will tend to rotate so as to be aligned with the electrical field (Figure 3-6). The tendency for molecules to become

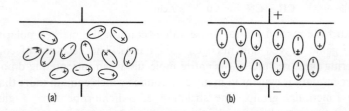

Figure 3-6 Behavior of polar molecules between the plates of an electrical condenser, (a) uncharged, and (b) charged so that the upper plate is positive.

aligned in this manner can be measured experimentally, and is characterized by the *dipole moment*. The dipole moment increases as the charge on each end of the molecule is increased, and also as the distance between the charges is increased. The conventional units for expressing dipole moments are Debye units (D), and the symbol for this property is μ. This direct measure of molecular polarity is of particular interest in attempting to understand the chemical behavior of organic compounds, for, as we shall see in Chapter 5, reactions tend to occur principally at sites where electronic charge is already concentrated. Some appreciation of the approximate range of dipole moments can be obtained from the following values for some familiar substances: H_2O, 1.9 D; HCl, 1.1 D; NH_3, 1.55 D; HCN, 3.0 D; SO_2, 1.6 D.

33

In Table 3–2 dipole moments are tabulated for several representative organic compounds, all of which have one structural feature in common, the presence of a methyl group (CH_3—) connected to a functional group. In every case, the positive end of the molecule is

Table 3–2

Dipole Moments of Methane Derivatives

Type of Compound	Structure	μ, D	Type of Compound	Structure	μ, D
Alkane	CH_3—CH_3	0.0	Amine	CH_3—NH_2	1.3
Alkyl Benzene	H₃C—⬡	0.4	Alcohol	CH_3—OH	1.7
			Ether	CH_3—O—CH_3	1.3
Alkyl Fluoride	CH_3—F	1.8	Ketone	CH_3—$\overset{\overset{\textstyle O}{\|\|}}{C}$—$CH_3$	2.9
Alkyl Chloride	CH_3—Cl	1.6			
Alkyl Bromide	CH_3—Br	1.8	Carboxylic Acid	CH_3—$\overset{\overset{\textstyle O}{\|\|}}{C}$—$OH$	1.7
Nitrile	CH_3—CN	4.0			

toward the methyl group. These values confirm the marked polarity of organic oxygen and nitrogen compounds. The necessity of considering the structure of the entire molecule when interpreting dipole moment data is evident in many compounds which contain more than one functional group. The structure of *p*-dichlorobenzene, Figure 3–7(c), for example, precludes the possibility of the molecule possessing

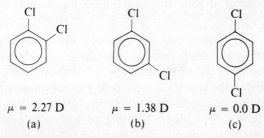

μ = 2.27 D (a) μ = 1.38 D (b) μ = 0.0 D (c)

Figure 3–7 Dipole moments for (a) *ortho-*, (b) *meta-*, and (c) *para*-dichlorobenzene.

a negative and a positive end. Rather, as the result of the electron-attracting ability of the two chlorines, it will be negative at *both* ends, and positive in the middle. There is no way of aligning such a molecule favorably in an electrical field, and consequently its dipole moment is zero. The other two isomers of dichlorobenzene, Figure 3–7(a) and (b), do not possess the same degree of symmetry and the chlorines do not work completely "against one another." The dipole moments therefore are sizeable, especially for the ortho isomer in which the joint effort of the two chlorines is most effective.

SOLUBILITY

The adage "like dissolves like" has served generations of chemists as a useful rule of thumb for predicting solubilities. By this is meant, simply, that a solid is most likely to dissolve in a liquid of similar chemical structure. On this basis, a nonpolar liquid, such as an alkane, is expected to be an exceptionally poor solvent for ionic compounds, as in fact it is. On the other hand, many classes of relatively nonpolar compounds, such as the hydrocarbons and alkyl halides, dissolve readily in hexane, or other alkanes. The high solubility of ionic substances in water is due to several factors, but they are all related to the high polarity of water. The two solvents, nonpolar hexane and polar water, are themselves almost completely mutually insoluble.

The "like dissolves like" rule can be rationalized on the basis that three factors are important in the solution process: (1) the separation of solvent molecules to make room for the solute, (2) the separation of solute molecules as they enter the solvent, and (3) the interaction of solvent and solute molecules. Solubility will be favored if the solvent-solute interactions are at least as strong as the attractions between solvent molecules and solute molecules, separately. In general, this is most likely to be true when the same types of intermolecular forces are dominant in each substance, and this implies a structural similarity between the solute and solvent molecules.

The solubility of various types of organic compounds in water provides a clear illustration of the importance of solvent-solute interactions. We know that the attractive forces between water molecules are strong, so that separation of them to make room for the solute molecules will be difficult. The organic substance will thus dissolve significantly in water only if the organic molecules strongly attract water molecules, and this in effect necessitates hydrogen bonding between the organic solute and water. The data in Table 3–3 for a group of compounds of similar molecular weight show the almost negligible solubility of those compounds which cannot participate in hydrogen bonding, i.e., the hydrocarbons and alkyl chlorides. Although they

35

possess no O—H or N—H, compounds such as the ethers, the ketones, and the esters possess oxygen atoms which can serve as hydrogen bond acceptors, or centers of negative charge toward which the water hydrogens may be pointed. Their solubility is increased accordingly in comparison with the hydrocarbons. In spite of its O—H, the alcohol is no more soluble than the isomeric ether, without an —OH, and we may conclude that the alcohol functions principally as a hydrogen bond acceptor in aqueous solution, also. In spite of the strong attractions between molecules in the amides and carboxylic acids, as reflected earlier in their high boiling points, these compounds show relatively high water solubilities, indicative of strong attractions also between the molecules of these compounds and water molecules. As expected, the introduction of two polar functional groups into the same molecule increases the water solubility accordingly, and the last two compounds in Table 3–3 are infinitely soluble in water.

Table 3–3

Solubility in Water of Some Organic Compounds of Similar Molecular Weight

Type of Compound	Structure	Mol. Wt.	Solubility*
Alkane	$CH_3(CH_2)_5CH_3$	100	0.005
Alkyl Chloride	$CH_3(CH_2)_4Cl$	107	0.02
Alcohol	$CH_3(CH_2)_5OH$	102	0.59
Ether	$CH_3(CH_2)_2O(CH_2)_2CH_3$	102	0.54
Ketone	$CH_3(CH_2)_3-\overset{\overset{\displaystyle O}{\|}}{C}-CH_3$	100	1.78
Ester	$CH_3CH_2CH_2-\overset{\overset{\displaystyle O}{\|}}{C}-OCH_3$	102	1.7
Carboxylic Acid	$CH_3(CH_2)_3\overset{\overset{\displaystyle O}{\|}}{C}-OH$	102	5.1
Amide	$CH_3(CH_2)_3-\overset{\overset{\displaystyle O}{\|}}{C}-NH_2$	101	4
Glycol (di-alcohol)	$CH_3-\overset{\overset{\displaystyle OH}{\|}}{C}H-CH_2CH_2CH_2-OH$	104	Infinite
Hydroxy-ester	$HO-CH_2CH_2-\overset{\overset{\displaystyle O}{\|}}{C}-OCH_2CH_3$	118	Infinite

* In units of g per 100 g of water at 20°C

CHAPTER **4**

Methods for Structure Determination

The organic chemist who has discovered a new compound has as his ultimate objective the assignment of a structural formula which is consistent with the physical and chemical properties of that compound. The structural formula is the model which is used to describe what elements and functional groups are present and the stereochemical manner in which they are linked together by chemical bonds. An understanding of the structural formula enables one to predict much of the chemical and physical behavior of the substance and to communicate this behavior to others for whom the structural formula has meaning. Structural formulae constitute the "language" of the organic chemist. In this chapter we shall describe the processes which enable him to attain his goal of structure assignment and examine some of the tools which he uses.

GENERAL PROCEDURE

A typical procedure which can lead to the assignment of a structural formula will consist of the following steps: (1) the isolation and purification of the compound; (2) an elemental qualitative and quantitative analysis; (3) the determination of a molecular formula; (4) the assignment of a structural formula based on spectroscopic and chemical evidence; (5) a synthesis of the compound to confirm the assigned structure.

ISOLATION AND PURIFICATION

The simplest plant or animal cell is a complex mixture of many chemicals, some present in such small amounts that they still remain undetected. Even the less complex mixtures obtained in routine laboratory work present interesting challenges to experienced chemical analysts. No specific procedure for isolation can be given which is applicable in every situation. We will attempt to survey some of the important laboratory techniques employed by the practicing chemist in the isolation and purification steps prior to structure elucidation.

Before isolation of a component can be attempted, it is often necessary to digest the material from which the component is to be isolated with a preliminary acid or base hydrolysis in order to break down polymeric material into isolable components. This treatment is necessary for the isolation of the components of proteins, carbohydrates, and nucleic acids, macromolecules which will be discussed in Chapter 7.

(a) Extraction

A partial separation of the desired compound can often be achieved by *extraction* with a suitable solvent. For the extraction of a *solid mixture,* such as plant or animal tissue, the solid is stirred or heated with such readily available solvents as methanol, ethyl ether, acetone, benzene, pyridine, chloroform, hexane, carbon tetrachloride, or dioxane. The solvent chosen is the one that will be most selective in removing the desired component. In this manner one may isolate caffeine from coffee, tea, or cola syrup, and cholesterol from egg yolk or gall stones.

Certain "rules of thumb" are usually followed in carrying out extractions. Inorganic materials and organic salts are generally insoluble in organic solvents but soluble in water. Compounds with five or less carbon atoms (with or without N and O) are appreciably soluble in water. The solubility of these compounds decreases as the number of carbon atoms increases. Though most organic compounds are mutually soluble to some extent, similarities in structure and polarity between solute and solvent increase the likelihood of mutual solubility (cf. Chapter 3).

The components of a *liquid mixture* may be separated by using an extracting solvent which is not miscible with the mixture. The liquid mixture is thoroughly shaken with the extracting solvent in a separatory funnel (Figure 4–1) and the lower layer is drawn off through the

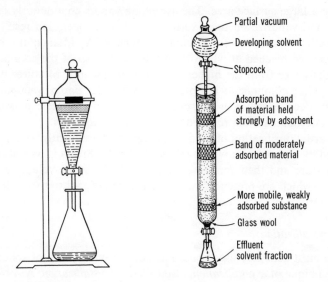

Figure 4–1 Separatory funnel with two immiscible solvent layers.

Figure 4–2 Diagram of a chromatographic separation by column chromatography.

stopcock. In general, the solute to be extracted should be more soluble in the extracting solvent than in the original solution. The solute will distribute itself between the two layers in the ratio of its solubility in each solvent. Repeated extractions greatly increase the efficiency of the separation. Commercial extraction equipment is available capable of performing a whole series of consecutive extractions, automatically mixing and transferring the solutions.

(b) Distillation

Distillation is a process of separation based on differences in vapor pressures of the components of a liquid mixture. The mixture is heated to the boiling point, the vapors are condensed in a cooling device, and the condensed liquid is collected as the distillation progresses. The vapors collected initially are richer in the lower boiling component, while those vapors collected last are concentrated with the less volatile components. Repeated distillation of the fractions collected (*fractional distillation*) results in increased purification. Very efficient distillation columns have been perfected which allow the fractional distillation to proceed in a single operation. This increased efficiency is achieved by passing the vapors through a column packed with inert material having a large surface area. The ascending vapors continuously condense and vaporize on these surfaces, each such operation resulting in a further separation of the liquid components. An ideal equilibrium state can be reached at which the vapor at the top of the column is essentially free from the higher boiling contaminants. Mixtures with high boiling components are often distilled under partial vacuum to prevent decomposition which could occur at atmospheric pressure. This procedure is often referred to as *vacuum distillation*.

A partial purification of a liquid mixture may frequently be accomplished by a process known as *steam distillation*. Steam is passed into the mixture and then condensed along with the steam-volatile components which are present in an amount proportional to their partial pressures.

(c) Crystallization

The most generally used procedure for the purification of solids is the technique of *crystallization*, also called *recrystallization*. A solvent is chosen in which the substance to be purified is readily soluble at the boiling point of the solvent, but very insoluble in the cold solvent. Insoluble impurities can be removed by filtering the hot solution, while the soluble impurities, if present in small quantities, remain dissolved in the cooled solution as the purified solute crystallizes. Successive recrystallizations increase the purity of the product.

(d) Chromatography

The term *chromatography* is used to describe that type of separation which occurs as a result of selective adsorption of compounds in a mixture as they are transferred between a mobile phase and a stationary phase. In *column chromatography* a cylindrical tube is packed with an adsorbent (immobile phase), such as powdered alumina, carbon, or cellulose, and the mixture to be separated is introduced onto the column, usually in the form of a solution. Fresh solvent (mobile phase) is then passed through the column and the components of the mixture are selectively adsorbed and dissolved by the stationary and the mobile phases. Because of differences in the rate of adsorption and solution, the components of the mixture pass down the column at different rates and adsorption bands containing these components appear on the column. When the components are not colored, the bands may be located with an appropriate chemical developing agent (see Figure 4–2, page 39).

To isolate the components of the mixture, the adsorbent may be removed, cut into sections, and the components washed from the sections with an appropriate solvent. An alternative procedure is to wash the column with solvent and to collect fractions of the effluent liquid which will yield the components upon evaporation. Figure 4–3 is a graph illustrating the type of separation which may be achieved.

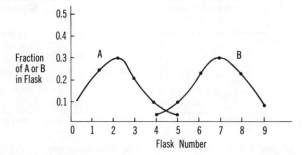

Figure 4–3 Graph showing relative amounts of *A* and *B* in effluent fractions.

In general, structurally similar components present greater difficulties in separation and the zones of separation become less distinct. Solvents may be selected ranging in polarity from *n*-hexane (nonpolar) to organic acids and bases (very polar), the choice being somewhat empirical, and the best results achieved through trial and error.

Originally reported in 1906 by the Russian Tswett, this separation technique has assumed great importance among modern methods of isolation and purification of organic compounds.

In *paper chromatography* cellulose, the chief constituent of paper, acts as the adsorbent. A solution of the mixture to be separated is introduced onto the paper in the form of a "spot" located near the edge of the paper. After the paper has been dried, it is suspended vertically, with the spot at the lower edge of the paper. An appropriate solvent mixture is allowed to ascend past the spot. The hydrated cellulose acts as the stationary phase and the solvent mixture as the mobile phase. As in column chromatography, the solute mixture is subjected to innumerable partitions between the two phases, and the components move along at different rates because of their different affinities for the phases. When the solvent front has traversed the paper, the paper is dried and the separate zones are located with the aid of ultraviolet light, iodine, or other chemical developing agent. To obtain greater resolution, the sheet may be turned 90° and placed, after the initial separation, in another solvent medium and the process

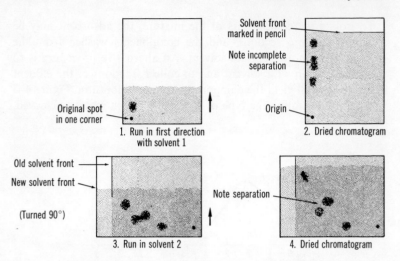

Figure 4–4 Two-dimensional paper chromatography.

repeated. This technique is sometimes referred to as two-dimensional paper chromatography (Figure 4–4).

The ratio of the distance traveled by a compound from the origin spot to the distance traveled by the solvent front is known as the R_f value for a compound. This value is constant under a given set of experimental conditions and can, therefore, be used for purposes of identification when R_f values of known compounds are available for comparison.

Paper chromatography is limited to the separation of milligram quantities (or less) of material and is used primarily as a method of qualitative analysis. However, the technique may be adapted to the quantitative estimation of micro-quantities of material as well.

A more recent innovation which has increased the versatility of this valuable laboratory technique is the use of specially prepared glass plates or plastic film on which has been placed a thin layer of adsorbent. Called *thin-layer chromatography* (t.l.c.), this modification permits the experimenter to select the type of adsorbent best suited to his needs while still retaining the advantages of paper chromatography. An additional advantage of thin-layer chromatography is the shorter time required to carry out the separation. Thin-layer sheets containing a variety of adsorbents are commercially available.

Another revolutionary chromatographic procedure which has added a new dimension to the analytical repertory of the organic chemist is *vapor phase chromatography* (v.p.c.). Also called *gas–*

liquid, or simply, *gas chromatography*, this method of analysis can be used for the qualitative or quantitative resolution of almost any mixture which has a significant vapor pressure within the temperature range of the instrument. A few microliters (or less) of the liquid to be analyzed are injected with a syringe into a compartment where the liquid is vaporized. A carrier gas, such as helium, carries the vapor through a long column packed with an inert, porous material coated with a nonvolatile liquid (stationary phase). The components of the mixture partition themselves between the liquid and the gaseous phase, and a resolution of the mixture takes place resulting in a difference in retention time for the gases passing through the column. As the effluent gases emerge, a detecting device sends a signal to a recorder which traces a chromatogram on a sheet of graph paper. The number of peaks traced indicates the number of components and the area underneath each peak is a measure of the quantity of each component present, relative to the other components in the mixture. A schematic diagram of the v.p.c. apparatus is shown in Figure 4–5 and a vapor-phase chromatogram is pictured in Figure 4–6.

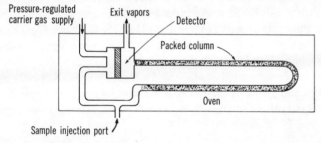

Figure 4–5 Schematic representation of the apparatus used for vapor-phase chromatography. (From Roberts-Caserio, *Basic Principles of Organic Chemistry*, W. A. Benjamin Inc., N.Y., 1964.)

Vapor-phase chromatography is currently used routinely in laboratory work as a means for establishing the purity of samples, as well as for qualitative and quantitative analysis. Instruments called preparative gas chromatographs have also been designed which permit the trapping of exit vapors so that small quantities of material may be obtained in a very pure state. For a more complete discussion of chromagraphic separations refer to references 1–5 (p.44).

(e) Electrophoresis

The separation of charged molecules or colloidal particles may be conveniently accomplished by means of a procedure known as *electro-*

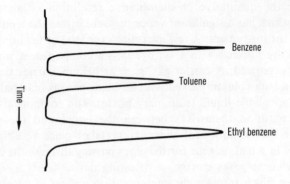

Figure 4–6 Vapor-phase chromatogram of a benzene-toluene-ethyl benzene mixture.

phoresis. Proteins and nucleic acids (see Chapter 7) are examples of macromolecules having numerous electrical charges. The magnitude and degree of charge is dependent upon the charged groups present in the molecule as well as upon the pH of the solution. Consequently, at a given pH a mixture of protein particles will migrate at different rates when placed in a medium between two electrodes. They may, therefore, be separated at staggered collection sites. Not only charge, but size and shape of the molecule as well, play a major role in determining the rate of migration. An excellent discussion of this topic may be found in reference (6).

CRITERIA OF PURITY

How does the organic chemist know when a compound he has isolated and purified is essentially free from impurities? The examina-

(1) K. Wiberg, *Laboratory Techniques in Organic Chemistry*, McGraw-Hill Book Co., Inc., New York, N.Y., 1960.

(2) "The Nature of Chromatography," H. Cassidy, *J. Chem. Educ.*, 33, 482 (1956).

(3) "Chromatography," W. Stein and S. Moore, *Scientific American*, March, 1951.

(4) "Gas Chromatography," R. Pecsok, *J. Chem. Educ.*, 38, 212 (1961).

(5) "Gas Chromatography," R. Keller, *Scientific American*, October, 1961.

(6) "Immunoelectrophoresis," C. Williams, *Scientific American*, March, 1960.

tion of a number of criteria is frequently necessary to establish purity. Pure liquids have narrow boiling ranges which do not change appreciably during successive distillations, and usually display one peak on a vapor-phase chromatogram. The *refractive index*, a measure of the ability of a liquid to refract incident light, may be readily measured with a refractometer. If repeated indices taken after successive purification steps remain unchanged, purity of the liquid is indicated. Solids normally have sharp melting points which remain constant after consecutive recrystallizations. Both solids and liquids give single spots on attempted separations with paper or thin-layer chromatography. An infrared spectrum (see page 54) is a kind of "molecular fingerprint" which can be used to detect the presence of impurities. If no change in the infrared spectrum is noted after a series of purification steps, it may be assumed that a compound is reasonably pure. Nuclear magnetic resonance and mass spectra (page 49) also provide informative spectroscopic evidence of purity. Methods of less general applicability employing such measurements as optical activity, radioactivity and other special properties of compounds are used on occasion to indicate purity of substances.

If a compound is known to be identical to a previously reported substance whose properties appear in the chemical literature, an authentic sample of the original compound is obtained and a direct comparison of properties and spectra is carried out.

QUALITATIVE ELEMENTAL ANALYSIS

Having established the purity of a compound, the organic chemist is now ready to determine its *empirical formula*. To do this he must obtain an accurate analysis of the relative weights (or percentages) of the elements present.

As stated in Chapter 2, the most common elements found in organic compounds, in addition to carbon and hydrogen, are oxygen, nitrogen, the halogens, and occasionally, sulfur and phosphorus.

Carbon and hydrogen are easily identified by heating the organic compound with cupric oxide in a test tube. Water can be observed to condense on the cooler portions of the test tube. If the gases evolved are allowed to bubble into a solution of barium hydroxide, barium carbonate precipitates upon reaction of carbon dioxide with barium hydroxide.

$$\text{Organic compoud} \xrightarrow[\Delta]{\text{CuO}} H_2O \uparrow + CO_2 \uparrow \xrightarrow{\text{Ba(OH)}_2} BaCO_3 \downarrow$$

Nitrogen, sulfur, and the halogens are most often present in the form of covalently bonded atoms. For most qualitative tests, therefore, it is necessary to convert them to ions in which form they are most conveniently identified. This transition can be carried out in a test tube reaction in which the organic compound is fused with metallic sodium converting nitrogen to CN^-, sulfur to S^{2-}, and the halogens to halide ions, X^- ($X = Cl$, Br, or I).

$$\text{Organic compound} \xrightarrow[\Delta]{\text{Na}} \begin{array}{l} \text{Na}^+,\ \text{CN}^- \\ 2\ \text{Na}^+,\ \text{S}^{2-} \\ \text{Na}^+\text{X}^- \end{array}$$
$$\text{(C, H, N, S, X)}$$

After the sodium fusion, the melt is dissolved in water and the solution may be tested for the presence of these ions. Cyanide ion can be detected by addition of Fe^{2+} and Fe^{3+} which combine with CN^- to form a blue precipitate, a complex called Prussian Blue. The composition of Prussian Blue is usually written as $KFe[Fe(CN)_6]$. The presence of sulfide ion may be observed by addition to the solution of lead acetate which unites with sulfide ion to form the black precipitate, lead sulfide. To test for the halides, the solution from the sodium fusion is acidified with nitric acid, boiled to remove CN^- and S^{2-} and then tested with Ag^+ in order to precipitate the halide ion as AgX. A confirmatory test for halogen may be applied on the original compound. The appearance of a green flame when a small portion of the compound is heated on a copper wire loop is evidence for the presence of a halogen. The latter test is known as the Beilstein Test.

QUANTITATIVE ELEMENTAL ANALYSIS

For a quantitative elemental analysis the organic chemist is frequently dependent on the microanalyst who specializes in routine analyses for the common elements present in organic compounds. With as little as 3–5 mg of sample a skilled analyst can obtain data which are accurate to ± 0.1–0.2% for the calculation of an empirical formula. A brief discussion of the general procedures used in these analyses follows.

The complete combustion of a weighed amount of an organic compound in oxygen over hot copper oxide converts carbon and hydrogen to carbon dioxide and water vapor. These gases are trapped in absorption tubes which are weighed before and after combustion. From the weight of carbon dioxide and water obtained, the weight of carbon and hydrogen in the original sample can be calculated. The calculations employed are familiar to students of general chemistry.

For nitrogen determination the procedure most often used is the Dumas method, since it is applicable to nearly all nitrogen compounds. A weighed quantity of the nitrogen compound is heated with copper oxide at approximately 1000°C. The gases formed, principally CO_2, H_2O, and N_2, are then swept by a stream of CO_2 over metal oxides to ensure complete combustion, and finally over hot copper. The latter treatment converts any oxides of nitrogen to nitrogen gas. The gases are then passed through a concentrated solution of KOH where the water and carbon dioxide are absorbed. The volume of nitrogen gas which remains is measured directly and, after correction for the vapor pressure of the KOH solution, is converted to standard temperature and pressure in the usual manner. From this volume and its corresponding weight the percentage of nitrogen in the sample can be calculated.

Reliable procedures are also known for the quantitative determination of halogens and sulfur. For the halogen determination the compound is heated with sodium peroxide (or sometimes nitric acid) in a sealed bomb. This procedure converts covalently bonded halogen to halide ion which may then be quantitatively estimated as AgX by the addition of Ag^+. By similar procedures sulfur may be converted to sulfate ion, phosphorus to phosphate ion, and quantitative estimations made by well established gravimetric procedures.

The percentage of oxygen is frequently determined by subtracting the sum of the percentages of the other elements present from one hundred.

A complete elemental analysis allows the calculation of the *empirical formula* of a compound by methods which are familiar to the reader. A molecular weight determination is necessary in order to write a *molecular formula* which represents the actual number of atoms of each element in a molecule.

MOLECULAR WEIGHT DETERMINATION

One or more methods for the approximate molecular weight determination of a compound are commonly performed in the general chemistry laboratory. The method of *vapor-density*, useful for gases and low-boiling liquids, involves a calculation based on the *ideal gas law*:

$$\text{Mol. wt.} = \frac{gRT}{PV}$$

In this calculation, g is the weight of the compound in grams, R is the gas law constant in liter atm $°K^{-1}$ mole^{-1}, T the Kelvin temperature, P the pressure in atmospheres, and V is the volume of the gas in liters. Known as the *Victor Meyer* method, this procedure is seldom used in practice because of its rather limited application to volatile compounds.

The *Rast* molecular weight determination is a cryoscopic method based on the principle that a mole of a nonelectrolyte will cause a predictable depression of the freezing point of a solvent. Camphor is frequently used because the freezing-point depression constant is high ($K_f = 39.7$). Thus a small quantity of solute will show a significant depression of the freezing point. Though the accuracy of this method is $\pm 10\%$, it is still useful where no greater accuracy is needed to distinguish between possible values for the molecular weight. Since the empirical formula has been precisely determined, the empirical formula weight can be divided into the approximate molecular weight to obtain a whole number quotient which, when multiplied by the more exact empirical formula weight, will give an accurate molecular weight. The calculation of the molecular weight in the Rast procedure may be done with the formula:

$$\text{Mol. wt.} = \frac{1000 \times g \times K_f}{\Delta t}$$

where g is the weight in grams of the unknown solute per gram of solvent, K_f is the freezing-point depression constant of the solvent, and Δt is the freezing-point depression in degrees.

Ebullioscopic or boiling-point methods for determining molecular weight are known which are dependent on the fact that a mole of a nondissociating solute will elevate the boiling point of a fixed quantity of solvent by a definite amount. Calculation of the molecular weight is carried out in much the same manner as in the Rast method.

An increasingly popular method for molecular weight determination is the *Signer method*, which is based upon the principle that the equilibrium vapor pressures above two equimolal solutions containing different solutes, but the same solvent, are identical. Weighed quantities of a known and an unknown solute are each placed in a volume of solvent in two chambers of a specially designed instrument. The two solutions, in contact with the same vapor phase are allowed to reach equilibrium, at which time the volumes of the solutions are accurately measured. The molecular weight of the unknown (M_x) may then be calculated as shown.

$$M_x = \frac{W_x \cdot M_k \cdot V_k}{W_k \cdot V_x}$$

48

The weights of the unknown and known compounds are W_x and W_k, respectively, the volumes V_x and V_k, and M_x and M_k represent the two molecular weights. The results obtained by this technique are accurate to $\pm 2\%$.

The most accurate means of molecular weight determination is the *mass spectrometer*. This instrument, although expensive, is available in larger university and industrial laboratories where analyses are made routinely. Even with compounds of limited volatility having molecular weights as high as 600, the mass spectrometer can produce an accurate molecular weight from a sample of 1 mg of material.

The principle of the mass spectrometer is familiar to students of general chemistry who have encountered its usefulness in the separation of atomic isotopes. In the determination of a molecular weight, molecules of an organic compound are bombarded by high energy electrons in a highly evacuated chamber. This treatment results in the fragmentation of the molecule into charged particles. This cleavage may be represented by the reaction:

$$R:R + 1e = R \cdot R^+ + 2e$$

These positive ions frequently have a charge (e) of 1 so that m/e is essentially the mass of the ion. The ions are accelerated and pass through a slit down a tube where they are sorted by an analyzing magnet according to their m/e values. Resolution of particles which differ only by a single mass number is possible, even with particles having a mass of several hundred. A mass spectrum may be obtained which indicates both the relative abundance of each particle and the m/e value. A typical mass spectrum appears in Figure 4–7.

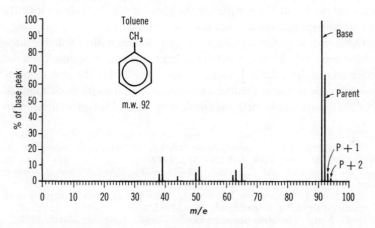

Figure 4–7 Graphic representation of the mass spectrum of toluene.

The peak with the highest intensity is referred to as the *base peak* (100%), and all other percentages are assigned relative to the base peak. The *parent peak* is the peak obtained by loss of one electron from the molecule and is the one from which the molecular weight is obtained. The other peaks result from further fragmentation of the molecule. Many of these particles can be identified from their m/e values. The fragmentation pattern is characteristic of the molecule being analyzed and thus the mass spectrum may also be used as a means of identification of organic molecules. An interesting study of the application of mass spectroscopy to the structural determination of the natural product, quebrachamine, is presented in reference (7).

The parent peak in the mass spectrum (M^+) is the peak with the highest mass number except for the peaks resulting from the presence of higher isotopes. Isotope peaks are present because some of the molecules contain the less common, heavier isotopes of carbon and hydrogen. In the toluene spectrum these peaks are designated as P + 1 and P + 2. The P + 1 peak may be due to $^{12}C_6{}^{13}C^1H_8{}^+$ or to $^{12}C_7{}^1H_7{}^2H_1{}^+$ with ^{13}C and ^2H being the less abundant isotopes of carbon and hydrogen. It is also possible, with the aid of tables containing the relative abundance of isotopes, to deduce the molecular formula from mass spectral data alone. The reader is referred to (8) for an excellent discussion of this procedure. Supplementary references on the applications of mass spectrometry are also worthy of the reader's attention, (9), (10). The full potential of the mass spectrometer in structure determination still remains to be realized. As fragmentation patterns emerge, from studies with known compounds, further information will be accumulated which may be applied toward structure elucidation. From these patterns the chemist will be able to identify the fragments and reconstruct the parent molecule.

Other methods for molecular weight determination will be mentioned here only briefly. Specialized techniques must be employed for macromolecules which, because of their low volatility and high insolubility, do not lend themselves to conventional methods of analysis. For these substances methods employing rates of sedimentation in an

---

[7] J. Roberts and M. Caserio, *Basic Principles of Organic Chemistry*, W. A. Benjamin, Inc., New York, N.Y., 1964, p. 1129.

[8] R. Silverstein and G. Bassler, *Spectrometric Identification of Organic Compounds*, 2nd Ed., John Wiley and Sons, New York, N.Y., 1967.

[9] E. Eliel, T. Prosser, and G. Young, "The Use of Mass Spectrometry in Organic Analysis," *J. Chem. Educ.*, 34, 72 (1957).

[10] O. Nier, "The Mass Spectrometer," *Scientific American*, March, 1952.

ultracentrifuge (11), *light-scattering measurements, viscosity, osmotic pressure, end-group analysis,* and *x-ray diffraction* are used. For more complete information on these techniques the reader is referred to (12).

THE STRUCTURAL FORMULA

From the empirical formula and the molecular weight a molecular formula may be calculated by methods already familiar to the reader. We are now ready to establish how these atoms are linked together in a structural formula, what functional groups are present, and what special stereochemical relationships, if any, exist. We shall see that both chemical and physical evidence are utilized in a manner which will enable us to construct a structural formula consistent with the properties of the compound.

Let us assume that we have isolated from a petroleum fraction a compound which is found to have the molecular formula C_8H_{10}. Now let us examine the chemical and physical evidence from which we may derive a unique structural formula for the compound.

The molecular formula itself provides a great deal of information about the structure: (1) The compound is obviously a hydrocarbon since only carbon and hydrogen are present. (2) The compound is unsaturated with respect to hydrogen since a compound with eight carbon atoms, if completely saturated with hydrogen, would have the formula, C_8H_{18} (C_nH_{2n+2}). This unsaturation suggests the presence of multiple bonds (alkene or alkyne) or perhaps an aromatic ring. For each double bond there are two less hydrogens (C_nH_{2n}) than in the saturated hydrocarbon; for each triple bond there are four less hydrogens (C_nH_{2n-2}). For each benzene ring there are eight less hydrogens than in a saturated hydrocarbon (compare benzene, C_6H_6, and *n*-hexane, C_6H_{14}). It can therefore be concluded that if our hydrocarbon has a benzene ring, all the unsaturation can be accounted for in terms of the ring alone.

CHEMICAL EVIDENCE FOR STRUCTURE

Some simple solubility tests coupled with several qualitative test tube reactions prove to be extremely useful. The compound dissolves very slowly in 95% H_2SO_4 but very readily in fuming H_2SO_4 ($H_2SO_4 + SO_3$). No color change is observed when the compound is treated with

[11] G. Gray, "The Ultracentrifuge," *Scientific American*, June, 1951.
[12] Weissberger, *Physical Methods of Organic Chemistry*, 3rd Ed., Vol. I, Interscience Publishers Inc., New York, N.Y., 1960.

a cold solution of $KMnO_4$ or a solution of Br_2 in CCl_4. The latter tests indicate the absence of alkenes and alkynes while the positive test with fuming sulfuric acid suggests the presence of an aromatic ring, since benzene rings are sulfonated by this reagent to give soluble sulfonic acids.

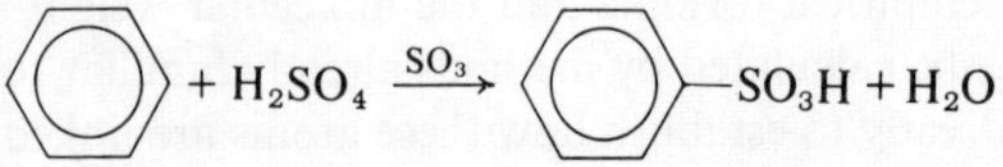

$$\text{C}_6\text{H}_6 + H_2SO_4 \xrightarrow{\ SO_3\ } \text{C}_6\text{H}_5{-}SO_3H + H_2O$$

On the basis of chemical evidence alone—reactions that are well known diagnostic tests to all organic chemists—we are led to conclude that our unknown hydrocarbon, C_8H_{10}, is a benzene derivative with one or two saturated side chains. The following structures may therefore be considered:

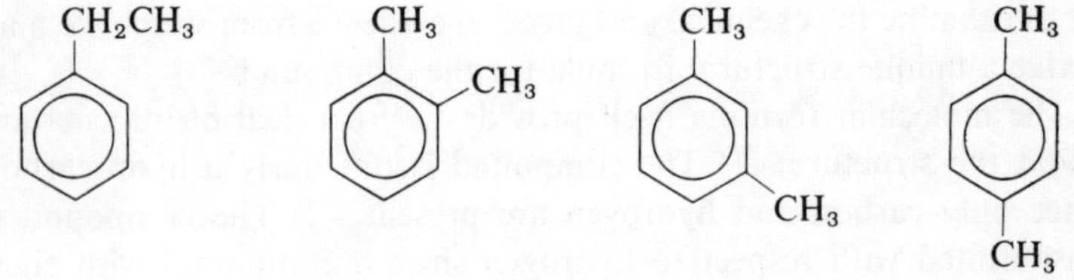

I	II	III	IV
ethyl benzene	*o*-xylene	*m*-xylene	*p*-xylene
b.p. 136°	b.p. 144°	b.p. 139°	b.p. 138°
$n_D^{20} = 1.4959$	$n_D^{20} = 1.5054$	$n_D^{20} = 1.4972$	$n_D^{20} = 1.4958$

Note that the boiling points and the refractive indices (n_D^{20}) are too similar to permit a decision based upon these criteria alone.

Before the advent of spectroscopic methods for structure elucidation, the organic chemist was dependent solely on chemical methods for identification. One such chemical method, still used to supplement spectroscopic methods in structure determination, is the *derivative* procedure. This approach can be applied when the unknown can be converted to a compound whose structure is known and whose properties have been reported in the chemical literature. Let us illustrate how this method might be used with compounds I–IV.

By a reaction familiar to organic chemists, side chains on aromatic rings may be oxidized by hot $KMnO_4$ or $K_2Cr_2O_7$ to corresponding carboxyl groups (—COOH). Compounds I–IV would thus be converted to the equivalent carboxylic acids, I′–IV′, whose melting points may be found in the chemical literature. The acid obtained upon

52

COOH   COOH   COOH   COOH

           COOH   COOH

                                                    COOH

    I′   II′   III′   IV′

m.p. 121°   m.p. 206°   m.p. 300°   m.p. 300°

oxidation could be identified by means of its melting point and the structure of the precursor therefore inferred. It is apparent that such a procedure would fail to differentiate between III and IV since both would be converted to acids having the same melting point. A second derivative is sometimes necessary when a derivative cannot be found which unequivocally identifies the starting material.

Though chemical methods are by no means outmoded, they have been greatly augmented by the spectroscopic techniques *infrared*, *ultraviolet*, and *nuclear magnetic resonance* spectroscopy. We shall look briefly at how these physical methods can aid us in the identification of our hydrocarbon C_8H_{10}. First, however, it will be instructive to consider some introductory theory on the nature of interactions between electromagnetic radiation and organic compounds.

ELECTROMAGNETIC RADIATION AND MATTER

The reader is probably already aware that the electromagnetic spectrum consists of radiation of varying wave lengths, each wave having a unique energy which is a function of the wave length. From the chart (Table 4–1), it is evident that higher values of energy are associated with the shorter wave lengths (λ) and higher frequencies or wave numbers (wave number = number of waves per cm = $1/\lambda$).

Organic molecules are not rigid but are in a state of ceaseless motion. In addition to external *rotational* and *translational* motion, there is the continual *stretching* and *bending* motion of bonds—*vibrational motion* —as well as *electronic* motion of the electrons themselves. According to quantum theory each type of motion is quantized (is associated with a specific amount of energy). Moreover, there are excited states for each type of motion which also are quantized. Molecules may be converted to these excited states by absorption of radiant energy if the radiant energy is of a magnitude which exactly corresponds to the difference in energy between one of the excited states and the original state. Infrared radiation has sufficient energy to cause excitation related

Table 4—1

The Electromagnetic Spectrum

Type of radiation	Wave length, λ, cm	Wave number cm^{-1}	Energy, erg
Radio	10^4	10^{-4}	2×10^{-20}
Radar	10	10^{-1}	2×10^{-17}
Infrared (IR)	3×10^{-2} to 7×10^{-5}	33 to 1.4×10^4	7×10^{-15} to 3×10^{-12}
Visible	8×10^{-5} to 4×10^{-5}	1×10^4 to 3×10^4	3×10^{-12} to 5×10^{-12}
Ultraviolet (UV)	4×10^{-5} to 10^{-5}	3×10^4 to 10^5	5×10^{-12} to 2×10^{-11}
X-rays	10^{-7} to 10^{-9}	10^7 to 10^9	2×10^{-9} to 2×10^{-7}
γ rays	2×10^{-10}	5×10^9	10^{-6}

to vibrational changes while the higher energy ultraviolet radiation is necessary for electronic excitation. Instruments, called *spectrometers*, have been developed which automatically scan molecules with light waves in the desired region of the spectrum and print out an absorption spectrum indicating the response of the molecule to the impinging radiation. The resulting pattern is characteristic of the individual molecule much as a fingerprint is characteristic of an individual person. Let us see how infrared and ultraviolet spectra may be used in the problem we are considering.

INFRARED SPECTROSCOPY

In Figure 4–8 we see the infrared spectrum of our compound C_8H_{10}. The interpretation of this spectrum may be done most competently by the expert spectroscopist but even the less experienced organic

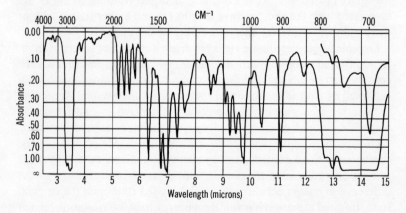

Figure 4–8 Infrared spectrum of ethyl benzene as a pure liquid.

54

chemist may interpret spectra with the aid of tables from reference sources such as (8). An authentic sample, if available, should always be used to substantiate identification. However, in the absence of an available "known," the organic chemist must rely on reported infrared data and his expertise acquired in the examination of many compounds. Table 4–2 contains a list of a number of some important functional groups and their absorption frequencies. The table is not meant to be comprehensive but is intended to illustrate how functional groups may be identified by means of their absorption frequencies.

Table 4—2

Characteristic Absorption Frequencies of Important Functional Groups

Functional Group	Absorption Wave length (microns)
OH	2.74–3.13
NH_2	2.86–2.94
CN	4.42–4.46
$R_2C{=}O$	5.35–6.50
COOH	3.03–4.00 (broad) and 5.68
COOR	5.71–5.76 and 7.70–10.00
$\backslash \quad /$ $C{=}C$ $/ \quad \backslash$	6.00–6.10

What does an inspection of Figure 4–8 tell us about our hydrocarbon? That it is aromatic is suggested by the absorption bands between 11 and 15 μ, bands which are normally absent in aliphatic hydrocarbons. (Absorption bands are reported in units of cm^{-1} or microns (μ) as illustrated in Figure 4–8.) The carbon–carbon stretching bands in the region 6–7 μ also have a pattern associated with aromatic compounds. Monosubstitution is indicated by the weak series, 5–6 μ. On the basis of infrared data we would conclude that our hydrocarbon is ethyl benzene, the only monosubstituted aromatic compound among our four possibilities. Since ethyl benzene is readily available, our conclusion could easily be verified by comparison with the IR spectrum of an authentic sample of ethyl benzene.

For a more complete discussion of the applications of infrared spectroscopy the reader should consult references (8), (13), and (14).

---

[13] G. Pimentel, "Infrared Spectroscopy: A Chemist's Tool," *J. Chem. Educ.*, **37**, 651 (1960).

[14] B. Crawford, "Chemical Analysis by Infrared," *Scientific American*, October, 1953.

NUCLEAR MAGNETIC RESONANCE SPECTROSCOPY

Another invaluable physical tool for structure determination is a *nuclear magnetic resonance* (NMR) spectrum. The NMR spectrum is obtained as a result of the interaction of radio-frequency radiation with the nuclei of certain atoms. The hydrogen nucleus as well as nuclei of certain other atoms of odd atomic number, has a magnetic moment along its axis of rotation, much as a spinning top has a mechanical moment about its axis of rotation. In the presence of an externally applied magnetic field, these magnetic moments can align themselves in a direction with the applied field (lower energy state) or against the field (higher energy state). The amount of energy necessary to effect a change from the lower energy state to the higher energy state depends on the environment of the hydrogen nucleus, that is, its position relative to other atoms in the organic molecule, as well as upon the magnetic field strength used. In actual practice a sample of the organic compound to be studied is placed in an applied magnetic field and subjected to radiation of constant radiofrequency. The strength of the magnetic field is gradually changed and absorption occurs at various field strengths where a current is generated and a signal is observed on a recorder. The resultant spectrum is a series of absorption peaks, each of which reflects the particular environment of a proton in a molecule. Exceptionally detailed information about molecular structure may be obtained from such spectra. The number of signals reveals the number of nonequivalent protons in the molecule. From the positions of the signals in the spectrum relative to an internal reference standard, one can identify the protons which give rise to the signal. The intensity of the signal, measured by the area underneath the peak, gives us the relative number of protons of each type. The manner in which the signal is split—*spin–spin coupling*—provides information about the nature of the environment of the proton, since neighboring protons are responsible for the splitting observed.

Let us look at the NMR spectrum (Figure 4–9) of ethyl benzene and observe what information might be derived from it. The three signals, two of which are split, indicate that our hydrocarbon has protons in three nonequivalent environments. The signal at 2.8τ is typical of signals obtained from protons on aromatic rings. The position of absorption is said to be downfield from the reference standard, tetramethylsilane, $(CH_3)_4Si$, and the position 2.8τ is called the *chemical shift* for aromatic protons. Frequently the signal from aromatic protons is split to a greater degree than is observed here due to dif-

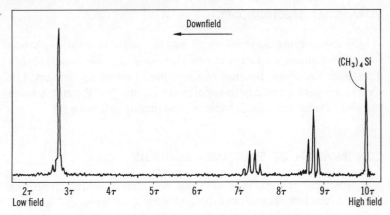

Figure 4–9 The NMR spectrum of ethyl benzene.

ferences in the environment of *ortho*, *meta*, and *para* protons. The simplest whole number ratio of the areas underneath the three signals is $5(2.8\tau):2(7.3\tau):3(8.8\tau)$. Thus, there are five aromatic protons and the ring is therefore monosubstituted.

The signal near 7.3τ arises from two protons on a carbon adjacent to a benzene ring. These "benzylic" hydrogens are known to absorb downfield from other alkyl hydrogens and have chemical shifts in the neighborhood of 7–7.8τ. The splitting of this signal into a quartet with areas $1:3:3:1$ is caused by an adjacent methyl group which, in turn, is split into a triplet $(1:2:1)$ by the hydrogens on the methylene group to which it is bonded. It is apparent from these data that our hydrocarbon is ethyl benzene and we must eliminate the other three structures as possibilities.

Experience with many compounds has indicated that protons with similar environments have the same chemical shift, though the molecules of which they are a part may be quite different. Interpretation of NMR spectra becomes increasingly difficult as the molecule becomes more complex. Nevertheless, NMR spectroscopy has proved to be a powerful tool for structure determination. More comprehensive treatments of the subject may be found in references (15), (16), and (17).

---

[15] J. Roberts, "Nuclear Magnetic Resonance Spectroscopy," *J. Chem. Educ.*, **38**, 581 (1961).

[16] J. Martin "NMR Spectroscopy as an Analytical Tool in Organic Chemistry," *J. Chem. Educ.*, **38**, 286 (1961).

[17] G. Pake, "Magnetic Resonance," *Scientific American*, August, 1958.

ULTRAVIOLET SPECTROSCOPY

Molecules having electrons which may be excited to stable excitation states (nonbonded valence electrons or those in multiple bonds) absorb ultraviolet radiation. Because of their more limited application, UV spectra are used primarily to supplement IR and NMR data. A more complete discussion of this topic is presented in reference (8).

CONFIRMATION OF STRUCTURE—SYNTHESIS

A structural analysis is usually not considered complete until the assigned structure is confirmed by synthesis. A molecule of "known" structure is constructed from simpler molecules using well understood, unambiguous reactions. The matching of the physical and chemical properties of the "unknown" with those of the synthetic product completes the identification. In our example a synthesis would be unnecessary since an authentic sample of ethyl benzene could be purchased. The topic of synthesis is considered in Chapters 6 and 7.

SUMMARY

In this chapter we have tried to describe the manner in which the structure of a compound is established. First, the compound must be isolated and purified. By means of a qualitative and quantitative analysis along with a molecular weight determination, a molecular formula is devised. Chemical and spectroscopic information is then utilized to construct a structural formula. Finally, an unambiguous synthesis confirms the assigned structure.

CHAPTER *5*

Organic Reactions and Mechanisms

Literally thousands of different reactions of organic compounds are known, ranging from those which are so general as to be applicable to most representatives of many classes of compounds to some which are peculiar to a single compound. Traditionally, in an attempt to organize this information, reactions have been classified into groups according to the functional groups involved in the reaction. This approach suffers from the disadvantage that it does not emphasize the similarity between reactions of different functional groups. As more information has become available concerning the manner in which organic reactions occur, classification of these reactions according to similarity in mechanism has become a viable alternative, or at least a supplement, to the functional group approach. In this chapter, the emphasis will be upon an understanding of the more common paths, or mechanisms, by which organic reactions occur. An attempt will be made to illustrate each type of reaction with a representative, but by no means comprehensive, set of examples drawn from a variety of functional groups.

Because of the very nature of the compounds with which it deals, organic chemistry is the chemistry of covalent bonds. In any organic reaction, one or more covalent bonds are either broken or formed, and this can serve as a starting point for the development of a set of arbitrary, but nevertheless very useful, reaction categories.

1. *Addition reactions* involve the combination of two (or more) reactants to form a new molecule, and result from the *formation* of one or more new covalent bonds. A familiar example from inorganic chemistry is the addition of water to carbon dioxide to form carbonic acid, resulting from the formation of two new bonds, one carbon–oxygen and one hydrogen–oxygen:

$$\ddot{\text{O}}{=}\text{C}{=}\ddot{\text{O}} + \text{H}_2\text{O} \rightarrow \ddot{\text{O}}{=}\overset{\overset{\textstyle \text{O}-\text{H}}{|}}{\text{C}}{-}\ddot{\ddot{\text{O}}}{-}\text{H} \tag{5-1}$$

2. *Elimination reactions* represent the reverse of addition reactions; i.e., reactions in which a molecule loses an atom or group of atoms as the result of *breaking* one or more covalent bonds. One familiar example from inorganic chemistry would, of course, be the reversal of reaction (5–1), above. Another example, involving the breaking of two P—Cl bonds, is reaction (5–2), often used to illustrate gas phase equilibrium:

$$\text{PCl}_5 \rightarrow \text{PCl}_3 + \text{Cl}_2 \tag{5-2}$$

3. *Substitution reactions*, in which a group in one of the reactants is replaced by a group from the other, involve both *breaking* the bond to the leaving group and *forming* a new bond to the entering group. Numerous examples of substitution reactions are familiar in inorganic chemistry and equations (5–3) and (5–4) are representative. Note that in each example, both bond breaking and bond formation must take

$$2\text{OH}^- + \text{Cl}_2 \rightarrow \text{OCl}^- + \text{Cl}^- + \text{H}_2\text{O} \tag{5-3}$$

$$\text{PCl}_3 + 3\text{H}_2\text{O} \rightarrow \text{P(OH)}_3 + 3\text{HCl} \tag{5-4}$$

place; the O—H bond is broken in reaction (5–3) and the O—Cl bond is formed, for example.

Each of the types of reactions described above will be examined in some detail in this chapter. First, however, since the breaking and formation of covalent bonds is involved in all these reactions, we shall consider the basic processes by which such bonds can be broken or formed.

FUNDAMENTAL PROCESSES—BOND BREAKING

The first question concerning the breakage of any covalent bond should probably be: "What happened to the electrons?" Obviously, when a covalent bond between two atoms, A and B, is broken, the cleavage can occur in any of three fundamental ways, in which the pair of bonding electrons either remains on A, remains on B, or is split "down the middle," with one electron remaining on each atom.

$$A : B \longrightarrow A{:}^- + B^+ \qquad (5\text{-}5)$$

$$A : B \longrightarrow A^+ + {:}B^- \qquad (5\text{-}6)$$

$$A {:} B \longrightarrow A{\cdot} + B{\cdot} \qquad (5\text{-}7)$$

Assuming that A—B represents an uncharged molecule, these three processes may be represented by equations (5-5), (5-6), and (5-7), respectively. Both (5-5) and (5-6) are termed *heterolytic* bond breaking processes, implying that the electron pair is not split, but moves as a pair with either atom A or B. The term *homolytic* bond breaking is applied to process (5-7) in which the bonding electrons are unpaired during the reaction. It is important to note that the products of heterolytic bond breaking are ions and that all electrons remain paired in the products, whereas the products of homolytic cleavage are uncharged, but each contains an unpaired electron. This distinction between heterolytic and homolytic bond cleavage is an important one, for it divides reactions into two rather different types, those in which electrons move in pairs and those in which they move singly.

Although covalent bonds do break "spontaneously" in some reactions, the necessary energy being provided either by heat or light, more commonly the bond is cleaved as the result of attack by a second reagent. Using the C—H bond as an example, the three modes of bond breaking described above are illustrated in equations (5-8) to (5-10), with the cleavage being assisted by an attacking reagent. (The symbols for the attacking reagents are meant to represent general types of species rather than specific substances and are further described on page 62). Reactions in which a reagent "plucks" an atom

$$R_3C{-}H + {:}N^- \rightarrow R_3C{:}^- + H{:}N \qquad (5\text{-}8)$$

$$R_3C{-}H + E^+ \rightarrow R_3C^+ + H{:}E \qquad (5\text{-}9)$$

$$R_3C{-}H + X{\cdot} \rightarrow R_3C{\cdot} + H{-}X \qquad (5\text{-}10)$$

from a molecule are often referred to as *abstraction* reactions. Since the types of attacking reagents in equations (5-8) to (5-10) are involved in other reactions besides abstraction reactions, we shall examine each of these processes in some detail.

In equation (5-8), the attacking reagent, $:N^-$, removes a hydrogen ion, H^+, from the substrate. In order to accomplish this, $:N^-$ must have an unshared pair of electrons (identified by two dots in the symbol) which can accept the hydrogen ion. Organic chemists refer to such a reagent as a *nucleophile*—i.e., a "nucleus-seeker"—since the pair of electrons on $:N^-$ is "seeking" a nucleus with which to form a covalent bond. Although the symbol $:N^-$ indicates a negative charge on the nucleophile, it should be stressed that nucleophiles may be either charged or uncharged, provided only that they possess the required pair of unshared electrons. This allows a vast number of compounds to be classed as potential nucleophiles, but among the more important in common organic reactions are:

$$:\overset{..}{\underset{..}{O}}\!\!-\!\!H^- \qquad H\!\!-\!\!\overset{..}{\underset{..}{O}}\!\!-\!\!H \qquad :NH_3 \qquad :C\!\!\equiv\!\!N:^- \qquad :\overset{..}{\underset{..}{I}}:^-$$

(Those familiar with either the Lewis or the Brönsted-Lowry concepts of acids and bases will recognize that the criterion for a substance to qualify as a potential nucleophile is identical to the definition of a base in either of these systems.)

The attacking reagent in equation (5–9) abstracts a hydrogen with its bonding electrons, i.e., a hydride ion. It is this pair of electrons which forms the new bond to E^+, and E^+ is thus termed an *electrophile* (electron-seeker). Again, the electrophile need not be charged, but it must be capable of accepting a pair of electrons to form a new bond, and many of the common electrophiles are positive ions:

$$H^+ \qquad Br^+ \qquad NO_2^+ \qquad SO_3 \qquad R_3C^+$$

(The organic chemist's term electrophile is synonymous with the Lewis definition of an acid, but not with the concept of Brönsted and Lowry.)

The peculiar characteristic of $X\cdot$, the attacking reagent in (5–10), is its possession of an unpaired electron, a property denoted by the term *radical*, or often *free radical*. A radical may be an individual atom, such as a chlorine atom, $Cl\cdot$, a relatively stable molecule like nitric oxide, $\cdot\overset{..}{N}\!\!=\!\!\overset{..}{O}$, or a fragment of an organic molecule, as with the product of reaction (5–10), $R_3C\cdot$. In the latter case, the carbon atom bearing the unpaired electron has only three groups attached, the lone electron occupies the fourth valence orbital of carbon, and the carbon atom is typically uncharged. Reaction (5–10) also shows the tendency for reactions of radicals to produce new radicals, so that a series of such reactions tend to occur sequentially, the product of one step serving as the initiating radical for the next.

62

INTERMEDIATES

In general, the organic products of the types shown in reactions (5–8) to (5–10) are not final reaction products but are short-lived *intermediates*, which may be expected to undergo further, rapid reaction leading eventually to stable products. These three species constitute the most important types of intermediates in nearly all organic reactions. They are similar in that each possesses three groups attached to the central carbon atom, but they differ in the number of electrons present in the fourth, "reactive" orbital of the carbon atom. The following comparison is pertinent:

$R_3C:^-$ a *carbanion* (negative ion with charge on carbon); reactive orbital contains two electrons; behaves as strong nucleophile in succeeding reactions.

R_3C^+ a *carbonium ion* (positive ion, charge on carbon); reactive orbital is empty, i.e., contains no electrons; behaves as strong electrophile in succeeding reactions.

$R_3C\cdot$ a *radical* (or free radical); contains one electron in reactive orbital; behaves as radical in succeeding reactions.

To recapitulate, using the parlance of the organic chemist, reaction (5–8) would be described as a proton abstraction by the nucleophile :N to form an intermediate carbanion, $R_3C:^-$. Similar statements could easily be constructed to describe (5–9) and (5–10).

Being as complex as they often are, organic molecules may possess several apparently similar sites at which reaction might occur. Even the relatively simple alkane shown below has four different types of C—H bonds (indicated by arrows), and the structure of the final reaction product in the reactions of the alkane will very likely depend

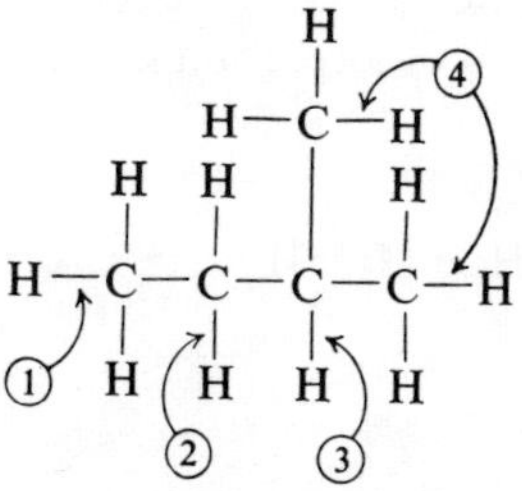

upon which of the C—H bonds is broken in the initial attack. One possibility, of course, would be a completely random one, in which each of the twelve C—H bonds would be equally likely to break. This, however, is rarely true experimentally, for there is usually a very great likelihood that reactions will occur at a specific position. In order to account for this, it seems reasonable to propose that the intermediates formed by removal of the various hydrogens (by whatever attacking reagent) would differ in their stabilities, and that *the most stable intermediate would be formed most easily.* This last assumption is not always true, but it turns out to be a very useful approximation for many reactions. In recent years, a great deal of study has been devoted to the effect of structural changes upon the stabilities of the three important types of intermediates described above—carbanions, carbonium ions, and radicals. The results of some of these studies will be mentioned later in connection with specific reactions.

FUNDAMENTAL PROCESSES—BOND FORMATION

Formation of new covalent bonds may be viewed simply as the reversal of bond breaking, and the pertinent question thus becomes, "Where did the electrons (forming the covalent bond) come from?" Again there are the three basic possibilities: both electrons come from the attacking reagent, both come from the (organic) substrate, or one electron may come from each. The first two, as in bond-breaking [compare equations (5–5) and (5–6)] are reactions of electron pairs, while the third involves unpaired electrons [compare equation (5–7)] and is thus a radical reaction.

Having examined the three types of bond breaking in very general terms, let us look at bond-forming processes in terms of some typical, specific examples. Equations (5–11) and (5–12) represent bond-forming steps in which the electron pair for the covalent bond comes from the attacking reagent, OH⁻ in (5–11) and H_2O in (5–12). Reaction (5–11) is typical of a reaction initiated by attack of a *nucleo-*

$$CH_3-\overset{\overset{\displaystyle :\ddot{O}}{\|}}{C}-OCH_3 + :\ddot{O}-H^- \longrightarrow CH_3-\underset{\underset{\displaystyle :\ddot{O}-H}{|}}{\overset{\overset{\displaystyle :\ddot{O}:^-}{|}}{C}}-OCH_3 \qquad (5\text{–}11)$$

$$CH_3-\underset{\underset{\displaystyle CH_3}{|}}{\overset{\overset{\displaystyle CH_3}{|}}{C^+}} + H-\ddot{O}-H \longrightarrow CH_3-\underset{\underset{\displaystyle CH_3}{|}}{\overset{\overset{\displaystyle CH_3}{|}}{C}}-\overset{+}{\underset{\diagdown H}{\overset{\diagup H}{\ddot{O}:}}} \qquad (5\text{–}12)$$

phile [cf. equation (5–8)] upon an unsaturated center. Since the carbon atom which is attacked already has its full complement of four covalent bonds, "something has to give" before the new pair of electrons can be accepted. What "gives," as indicated by the small curved arrow, is one of the pairs of electrons in the carbon–oxygen double bond, which moves up onto the oxygen making room for a new pair of electrons on carbon. Since the carbon–oxygen bond was originally a double bond, it can lose one of its pairs of electrons without breaking the bond completely, whereas if it had been a single bond, this would not be possible. Consequently, when reactions are initiated by bond formation in this manner, the new bond is nearly always formed at an unsaturated center. Attention should also be directed to the charge balance in this reaction, the attack of a negatively charged nucleophile upon a neutral substrate producing an intermediate with a negative charge (on oxygen). Reaction (5–12) is typical of reactions of carbonium ions, a type of intermediate which we discussed earlier [cf. equation (5–9)]. It differs from reaction (5–11) in that the organic substrate is *not* a stable organic molecule but a short-lived intermediate, and it contains a vacant orbital. Therefore, nothing needs to "give" and it seems a very natural thing for this empty orbital to "grab" one of the pairs of electrons on a water molecule to form a new C—O bond. Again, the charge balance should not be overlooked, nor the fact that in sharing a pair of electrons from oxygen to carbon, the positive charge shifts from carbon to oxygen.

When a reaction is initiated by the attack of an *electrophile* upon a molecule, as in equation (5–13), the electrons for the new bond are both furnished by the organic substrate. As in the reaction initiated by nucleophilic attack (5–11), it is significant that reaction (5–13) takes

$$H_3O^+ + CH_2 = C\begin{smallmatrix}CH_3\\CH_3\end{smallmatrix} \longrightarrow H_2O + H—CH_2—C^+\begin{smallmatrix}CH_3\\CH_3\end{smallmatrix} \qquad (5\text{–}13)$$

$$:\ddot{C}l—\ddot{C}l: + :\bar{C}H_2—\overset{O}{\overset{\|}{C}}—CH_3 \longrightarrow :\ddot{C}l:^- + :\ddot{C}l—CH_2—\overset{O}{\overset{\|}{C}}—CH_3 \quad (5\text{–}14)$$

place at an unsaturated center, for the attacking proton (H^+) must "steal" a pair of electrons from the carbon–carbon double bond (small curved arrow in equation 5–13). Only because there were initially two pairs of electrons in this bond is there still a bond between the carbon atoms after the "theft." Such an attack by an electrophile characteristically produces a *carbonium ion* intermediate, as it does here, for the shift of the pair of electrons away from one carbon leaves that carbon atom with a vacant orbital and consequently a positive charge. Equation (5–14) describes a reaction in which the electrophile is Cl_2; this reaction differs from (5–13) in that the Cl_2 does not initiate an attack upon a stable organic molecule, but rather reacts with a carbanion intermediate formed in a preceding step. Note again that the pair of electrons for the new C—Cl bond comes from the organic substrate—specifically, the pair of electrons in the reactive orbital which accounts for the negative charge of the carbanion. In order for the Cl_2 to function as an electrophile, the Cl—Cl bond must break as indicated, the bonding pair of electrons remaining on the unattached chloride ion.

Several bond-forming steps involving radicals are shown in equations (5–15) to (5–17). Once again, that reaction in which a bond-forming step initiates the reaction of the organic substrate occurs at an unsaturated site (reaction (5–15)). The small arrows indicate the fact that the π-electrons in the double bond must part company, one helping to form the new C—Cl bond, the other occupying the reactive

$$:\ddot{C}l\cdot + CH_2\!=\!CH_2 \longrightarrow :\ddot{C}l-CH_2-\dot{C}H_2 \qquad (5\text{--}15)$$

$$Cl-CH_2-\dot{C}H_2 + :\ddot{C}l\!\mid\!\ddot{C}l: \longrightarrow Cl-CH_2-CH_2-Cl + :\ddot{C}l\cdot \qquad (5\text{--}16)$$

$$Cl-CH_2-\dot{C}H_2 + \dot{C}H_2-CH_2-Cl$$
$$\longrightarrow Cl-CH_2-CH_2-CH_2-CH_2-Cl \qquad (5\text{--}17)$$

orbital in the product *radical* (cf. p. 63). It was observed earlier that reactions of radicals tend to produce new radicals, and both (5–15) and (5–16) attest to this fact. What appears to be a very promising method of bond formation, the coupling of the "odd" electrons on two radicals (equation (5–17)), is less common than one might expect, for radicals are highly reactive intermediates, with very short "life expectancies." Consequently, there are rarely many radicals present at any one time, and the probability of two of them bumping into one another during their brief life-span is very small.

EFFECTS OF BOND POLARITY

The reader may rightfully feel, at this point, that we have succeeded in showing that virtually any reagent, be it nucleophile, electrophile, or radical, can potentially react with any organic substrate, in a step involving either bond breaking or bond formation. But the question is not only whether a reaction is conceivable, but whether, in fact, one occurs—or at least, whether one is probable. The essence of sorting out the probables from the possibles, especially in those reactions in which the electrons move as pairs, lies in the familiar attraction of opposite electrical charges and the repulsion of like charges. If a bond is already polar, then when that bond breaks it will very probably break in such a manner as to accentuate its polarity. The electrons in a C—Cl bond, for example, due to the high electronegativity of chlorine, are displaced significantly toward chlorine (compare the dipole moment data, Table 3–2), as indicated by the partial charges in equations (5–18) and (5–19). When the C—Cl bond breaks, whether spontaneously or as the result of attack by a second reagent, it can be expected to break "with the polarity," as in (5–18), and *not* as in (5–19).

$$CH_3-\underset{\underset{CH_3}{|}}{\overset{\overset{CH_3}{|}}{C}} \overset{\delta+}{-} Cl \overset{\delta-}{} \longrightarrow CH_3-\underset{\underset{CH_3}{|}}{\overset{\overset{CH_3}{|}}{C^+}} + Cl^- \qquad (5\text{--}18)$$

$$CH_3-\underset{\underset{CH_3}{|}}{\overset{\overset{CH_3}{|}}{C}} \overset{\delta+}{-} Cl \overset{\delta-}{} \xrightarrow{\;\;\times\;\;} CH_3-\underset{\underset{CH_3}{|}}{\overset{\overset{CH_3}{|}}{C^-}}{:} + Cl^+ \qquad (5\text{--}19)$$

Returning to a previous example (equation (5–11)), is this not only a possible, but also a probable reaction? Is the alternative, involving attack of the nucleophilic OH$^-$ at oxygen (equation (5–20)) equally probable? The answer to these questions comes from a consideration of the nature of the carbon–oxygen double bond, which on the basis

$$CH_3-\overset{\overset{\displaystyle :\ddot{O}^{\delta-}}{\|}}{\underset{\delta+}{C}}-O-CH_3 + OH^- \longrightarrow CH_3-\overset{\overset{\displaystyle :\ddot{O}:^-}{|}}{\underset{\underset{OH}{|}}{C}}-O-CH_3 \qquad (5\text{--}11)$$

$$CH_3-\overset{\overset{\displaystyle :\ddot{O}^{\delta-}}{\|}}{\underset{\delta+}{C}}-O-CH_3 + OH^- \xrightarrow{\;\;\times\;\;} CH_3-\overset{\overset{\displaystyle :\ddot{O}-OH}{|}}{C}-O-CH_3 \qquad (5\text{--}20)$$

of electronegativities (Table 2–2) or dipole moment data (Table 3–2) is strongly polarized toward oxygen. Using the attraction of unlike charges as a guide, reaction (5–11) appears probable, since the partially positively charged carbon atom will attract the electron pair of the nucleophile, OH⁻. By the same token, the improbability of (5–20) is based upon mutual repulsion of the negative end of the C—O dipole and the electron pairs on OH⁻.

AN INTERIM SUMMARY

Before attempting a survey of some important reactions which involve the types of fundamental processes we have described, it may be well to summarize the major terms which have been used and the processes described. It is suggested that the reader review the first part of this chapter, if necessary, so that he will have a working knowledge of these concepts at his disposal as he confronts some of the types of reactions which characterize organic chemistry.

Most organic reactions involve a series of simple steps in which individual bonds are *formed* or *broken*. Bond breaking may occur spontaneously, or as the result of *abstraction* of an atom from the *substrate* by a second reagent. The attacking reagent may be an *electrophile*, a *nucleophile*, or a *radical*, and the pair of electrons in the bond being broken will correspondingly leave with the atom being abstracted, remain on the substrate, or become unpaired, with one electron leaving and the other staying. Most reactions involve *either* a series of *heterolytic* (or polar) steps, in which the electrons move as pairs, *or* a series of *homolytic* steps, in which the electrons move singly. The common intermediates in heterolytic processes are either *carbonium ions* or *carbanions*, while homolytic reactions involve *free radicals* as the unstable intermediates.

ADDITION REACTIONS

Saturated organic compounds, i.e., compounds containing no double or triple bonds, are so named because nothing else can be added to them. Each carbon is already attached to four other atoms, so that there is simply "no room" for the addition of any reagent which would necessitate the formation of an additional bond. Therefore, our concern in this section will be with unsaturated compounds, both those containing carbon–carbon double or triple bonds and those containing carbon–oxygen double bonds (see functional groups inside back cover).

68

The addition of some unspecified reagent to a double bond may be described by the general equation (5–21). It is clear that, from the standpoint of the organic substrate, this reaction involves the forma-

$$\diagdown \!\!\!\underset{\diagup}{C}\!\!=\!\!\underset{\diagdown}{C}\!\!\diagup + \text{ X—Y} \rightarrow -\overset{\text{X}}{\underset{|}{\text{C}}}-\overset{\text{Y}}{\underset{|}{\text{C}}}- \tag{5–21}$$

tion of two new bonds, C—X and C—Y (the change from C=C to C—C will not be considered "bond breaking" for purposes of our analysis here). Clearly also, both bonds may be formed simultaneously, or they may form sequentially in separate steps. Although simultaneous, or "one-step," additions occur, "two-step" additions are much more common and the former will not be considered in this book.

Alkenes

Addition reactions are *the* characteristic reactions of alkenes. In examining a hydrocarbon of uncertain structure, a small amount of bromine is often added, and if the color of Br_2 rapidly disappears [reaction (5–22)], the compound is assumed to contain a double bond. This is a typical two-step addition reaction, which is initiated (5–23) by an electrophilic attack by bromine upon the double bond to form a carbonium ion intermediate. The carbonium ion, a highly reactive

$$CH_3\text{—CH}\!\!=\!\!CH_2 + Br_2 \rightarrow CH_3\text{—}\overset{\text{Br}}{\underset{|}{\text{CH}}}\text{—}\overset{\text{Br}}{\underset{|}{\text{CH}_2}} \tag{5–22}$$

$$CH_3\text{—CH}\!\!=\!\!CH_2 + Br_2 \rightarrow CH_3\text{—}\overset{+}{\text{CH}}\text{—}\overset{\text{Br}}{\underset{|}{\text{CH}_2}} + Br^- \tag{5–23}$$

$$CH_3\text{—}\overset{+}{\text{CH}}\text{—}\overset{\text{Br}}{\underset{|}{\text{CH}_2}} + Br^- \rightarrow CH_3\text{—}\overset{\text{Br}}{\underset{|}{\text{CH}}}\text{—}\overset{\text{Br}}{\underset{|}{\text{CH}_2}} \tag{5–24}$$

intermediate, is susceptible to attack by the first nucleophile which comes along, which in this example is bromide ion (5–24). If another nucleophile is present, then part, or all, of the reaction of the carbonium ions may be diverted away from bromide ion to form different products. In the two examples shown in (5–25), it should be noted that the first step is identical to (5–23), but the carbonium ion has been deliberately "trapped" by the addition of water in one case, and sodium chloride in the other. (The last step in the top line of (5–25)

$$CH_3CH{=}CH_2 + Br_2$$

$$\xrightarrow{+H_2O} CH_3\overset{\overset{+}{O}H_2}{\underset{|}{C}}HCH_2Br \xrightarrow{+H_2O} CH_3\overset{\overset{OH}{|}}{C}HCH_2Br + H_3O^+$$

$$CH_3\overset{+}{C}HCH_2Br + Br^-$$

$$\xrightarrow[+Na^+]{Cl^-} CH_3\overset{\overset{Cl}{|}}{C}HCH_2Br + Na^+$$

$$(5\text{--}25)$$

involves transfer of a proton from oxygen in the product to an oxygen atom of a water molecule. Such proton transfers are very common, and are normally rapid and reversible in aqueous solution.) Other electrophiles can replace bromine in initiating steps comparable to (5–23), and on this basis we can understand the reactions of alkenes with a wide variety of strongly acidic reagents, some examples of which are shown in (5–26). The intermediates in equations (5–26) have been bracketed to emphasize the fact that the same carbonium ion may be generated by a variety of acidic reagents, the electrophile in each case being the hydrogen ion. As before, the carbonium ion will react quickly with whatever nucleophile is available, commonly the anion from which the hydrogen ion was removed in the first step.

$$CH_3{-}CH{=}CH_2 + HBr \longrightarrow [CH_3{-}\overset{+}{C}H{-}CH_3] + Br^- \longrightarrow CH_3{-}\overset{\overset{Br}{|}}{C}H{-}CH_3$$

$$CH_3{-}CH{=}CH_2 + H_2SO_4 \longrightarrow [CH_3{-}\overset{+}{C}H{-}CH_3] + HSO_4^- \longrightarrow CH_3{-}\overset{\overset{OSO_3H}{|}}{C}H{-}CH_3$$

$$CH_3{-}CH{=}CH_2 + H_3O^+ \longrightarrow [CH_3{-}\overset{+}{C}H{-}CH_3] + H_2O \longrightarrow CH_3{-}\overset{\overset{+OH_2}{|}}{C}H{-}CH_3$$

$$CH_3{-}\overset{\overset{OH}{|}}{C}H{-}CH_3 + H_3O^+ \quad \Big\downarrow {+H_2O}$$

$$(5\text{--}26)$$

It may have occurred to the reader that a seemingly arbitrary option was exercised in writing the carbonium ion in (5–26), since either of two intermediates is possible, depending upon which carbon is attacked by the electrophile. As shown in (5–27) for the addition of HBr, a change in the structure of the intermediate is critical, for it would result in a different product. In fact, however, it was not an arbitrary whim which dictated the choice of one of these intermediates; it was guided by the principle that the more stable intermediate will form more readily. It has been amply demonstrated that alkyl groups

70

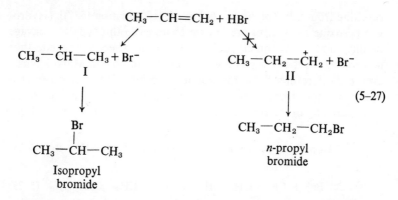

$$CH_3-CH=CH_2 + HBr$$

$$CH_3-\overset{+}{C}H-CH_3 + Br^- \qquad\qquad CH_3-CH_2-\overset{+}{C}H_2 + Br^-$$
$$\text{I} \qquad\qquad\qquad\qquad\qquad \text{II}$$

(5–27)

Br
|
$$CH_3-CH-CH_3 \qquad\qquad CH_3-CH_2-CH_2Br$$
Isopropyl   *n*-propyl
bromide   bromide

attached to the charge-carrying carbon atom increase the stability of a carbonium ion. In I, there are two alkyl ($-CH_3$) groups attached to the positive carbon, while in II there is only one group ($-CH_2CH_3$). The expected greater stability of I thus makes it the intermediate of choice in all additions to propylene initiated by attack of H^+.

Since the π-electrons in a double bond stick out like bananas from the central C—C bond in an alkene (structure XI, Chapter 2), they form a region of negative charge which is "ripe for plucking" by an approaching electrophile. Addition reactions may also be initiated by nucleophilic attack, but such reactions are not common among alkenes. This fact may be ascribed to a repulsion of like charges, the electron pair of the attacking nucleophile being repelled by the π-electrons of the double bond.

A curious discrepancy attracted the attention of many early investigators of the addition of HBr to propylene (reaction (5–27)). Some reported the reaction to go smoothly, producing isopropyl bromide, but others reported obtaining the "wrong" product, *n*-propyl bromide. The controversy was resolved in 1933 in a classic paper by Kharasch and Mayo, which showed that the "wrong" product was obtained if the reaction mixture contained trace amounts of catalytic impurities (specifically, derivatives of hydrogen peroxide), or if the mixture was strongly illuminated during the reaction. To account for the formation of *n*-propyl bromide, an alternative mechanism was proposed in which the reaction is initiated by *attack of a radical* ($Br\cdot$) upon the double bond [compare equation (5–15)]. The reaction is completed when the radical intermediate (III) abstracts a hydrogen atom from HBr [compare equation (5–16)]. The complete sequence of steps is shown in equations (5–28) to (5–31). Reaction (5–28) is a schematic representation of what is termed an *initiation* process, resulting from a *homolytic bond cleavage* [cf. equation (5–7)]. (Hydrogen peroxide derivatives are known to undergo this type of cleavage readily, and many other substances do so when irradiated, thus accounting for the catalysis observed by Kharasch and Mayo.) Whatever radical results from the initial bond-breaking may abstract a hydrogen atom from H–Br to form a bromine atom. The key to an understanding of the significance of this initiation step lies in reactions

$$\text{Homolytic bond breaking} \longrightarrow X\cdot \xrightarrow{+\,HBr} X\!-\!H + Br\cdot \quad (5\text{–}28)$$

$$Br\cdot \; + \; CH_2\!\!=\!\!CH\!-\!CH_3 \longrightarrow Br\!-\!CH_2\!-\!\overset{\cdot}{C}H\!-\!CH_3 \quad (5\text{–}29)$$
$$\text{III}$$

$$Br\!-\!CH_2\!-\!\overset{\cdot}{C}H\!-\!CH_3 + H\!-\!Br \longrightarrow Br\!-\!CH_2\!-\!\overset{\overset{\displaystyle H}{|}}{C}H\!-\!CH_3 + Br\cdot \quad (5\text{–}30)$$
$$\text{III} \qquad\qquad\qquad n\text{-propyl bromide}$$

$$Br\!-\!CH_2\overset{\cdot}{C}HCH_3 + CH_3\overset{\cdot}{C}HCH_2Br \longrightarrow Br\!-\!CH_2\overset{\overset{\displaystyle CH_3}{|}}{C}H\!-\!\overset{\overset{\displaystyle CH_3}{|}}{C}HCH_2\!-\!Br \quad (5\text{–}31)$$

(5–29) and (5–30). Every time a bromine atom is consumed in (5–29), another is generated by the succeeding reaction (5–30), and this second bromine atom starts reaction (5–29) again. Each time through the cycle of reactions (5–29) and (5–30) a molecule of the product, *n*-propyl bromide, is formed. This cycle is destined to continue until a *termination* reaction, such as (5–31), removes two of the radicals from the reaction. We have already seen (p. 66) that bond-forming reactions like (5–31) are very improbable, due to the difficulty of two radicals locating each other. Thus, a single initiation step may trigger a *chain* reaction which proceeds through steps (5–29) and (5–30) hundreds or even thousands of times, forming a corresponding number of *n*-propyl bromide molecules, before the cycle is stopped by a termination step.

Addition reactions initiated by radicals constitute an important group of reactions, including radical *polymerization*, which is the very essence of the enormous synthetic plastics industry. The key step in this process [reaction (5–32)] is the formation of a new C—C bond by the addition of an intermediate radical (similar to III) to a second

$$X\!-\!CH_2\overset{\cdot}{C}H_2 + CH_2\!\!=\!\!CH_2 \rightarrow X\!-\!CH_2CH_2CH_2\overset{\cdot}{C}H_2 \quad (5\text{–}32)$$

C—C double bond. The mechanism of radical polymerization is described in more detail in Chapter 7. An extensive treatment of free radical reactions may be found in reference (1).

Aromatic Rings

It was the failure of so-called aromatic compounds to undergo the addition reactions characteristic of double bonds which led to the postulate of a unique structure of the aromatic ring. Addition to the aromatic ring would require the breaking up of the π-electron system of the aromatic ring. The stability of this aromatic π-system prevents addition, but we shall see that it allows alternative reactions under much the same conditions [e.g., reaction (5–49)].

Carbonyl groups

The carbon–oxygen double bond, known as a *carbonyl group*, occurs in several common functional groups: for example those in ketones and aldehydes, carboxylic acids, esters, and amides. As discussed earlier, this is a highly polar double bond (see dipole moment data, Table 3–2), with the oxygen being the negative end of the dipole. The oxygen is thus a prime candidate for electrophilic attack and is particularly susceptible to protonation, as in the first step of reaction (5–33). The resulting carbonium ion reacts with a variety of nucleophiles to produce addition products, as illustrated in (5–33) for the

$$CH_3\overset{\overset{\displaystyle \cdot\cdot\atop \displaystyle \cdot O\cdot}{\|}}{C}CH_3 + H_3O^+ \rightleftharpoons CH_3\overset{\overset{\displaystyle :O-H}{|}}{\underset{+}{C}}CH_3$$

Acetone

$$\text{(5–33)}$$

$+H_2O \qquad +NH_2OH$

$$CH_3\overset{\overset{\displaystyle OH}{|}}{\underset{\underset{\displaystyle OH}{|}}{C}}CH_3 + H_3O^+ \xrightleftharpoons{+H_2O} CH_3\overset{\overset{\displaystyle :O-H}{|}}{\underset{\underset{\displaystyle +}{\underset{\displaystyle H-\overset{\cdot\cdot}{O}-H}{|}}}{C}}CH_3 \quad CH_3\overset{\overset{\displaystyle :O-H}{|}}{\underset{\underset{\displaystyle +}{\underset{\displaystyle NH_2OH}{|}}}{C}}CH_3 \xleftarrow{+H_2O} CH_3\overset{\overset{\displaystyle OH}{|}}{\underset{\underset{\displaystyle NHOH}{|}}{C}}CH_3 + H_3O^+$$

ketone, acetone. These reactions are general for other types of carbonyl compounds, also, and for other nucleophiles, as well. The

---

(1) W. Pryor, *Introduction to Free Radical Reactions*, Prentice-Hall, Inc., Englewood Cliffs, N.J., 1966.

carbon–oxygen double bond is exceptionally stable, however, and for the most part, although the reactions occur readily, the products are not sufficiently stable to be isolated; i.e., the position of equilibrium lies to the left in reactions of this type.

The marked polarity of the carbonyl group leaves the carbon atom open to initial attack by nucleophiles as well. The same overall reactions shown in (5–33) can often be effected in reverse order, nucleophilic attack preceding electrophilic, as shown in (5–34) for the addition of water. Reaction (5–35) also occurs by initial nucleophilic

$$
\underset{\cdot\cdot}{CH_3-\overset{\overset{\cdot\cdot}{O}\cdot}{\underset{\|}{C}}-CH_3} + OH^- \rightleftharpoons CH_3-\overset{\overset{:\ddot{O}:^-}{}}{\underset{\underset{OH}{|}}{C}}-CH_3 \xrightarrow{+H_2O}
$$

$$
CH_3-\overset{OH}{\underset{\underset{OH}{|}}{C}}-CH_3 + OH^- \qquad (5\text{–}34)
$$

$$
CH_3-\overset{\overset{\cdot\cdot}{O}\cdot}{\underset{\|}{C}}-CH_3 + CN^- \rightleftharpoons CH_3-\overset{:\ddot{O}:^-}{\underset{\underset{CN}{|}}{C}}-CH_3 \xrightarrow{+HCN}
$$

$$
CH_3-\overset{OH}{\underset{\underset{CN}{|}}{C}}-CH_3 + CN^- \qquad (5\text{–}35)
$$

attack, and the products may be isolated in the case of aldehydes and many ketones. Included among the nucleophilic additions to carbonyl groups also are two very important reactions of carbanion (or carbanion-like) reagents. In the first equation (5–36), the nucleophile

$$
CH_3-\overset{O}{\overset{\|}{C}}-CH_3 + \underset{IV}{\bar{C}H_2\overset{O}{\overset{\|}{C}}CH_3} \xrightleftharpoons{+H_2O} CH_3\overset{O}{\overset{\|}{C}}CH_3 + OH^-
$$

$$
(5\text{–}36)
$$

$$
CH_3-\overset{O^-}{\underset{\underset{CH_2-\overset{O}{\overset{\|}{C}}-CH_3}{|}}{C}}-CH_3 \xrightarrow{+H_2O} CH_3-\overset{OH}{\underset{\underset{CH_2-\overset{O}{\overset{\|}{C}}-CH_3}{|}}{C}}-CH_3 + OH^-
$$

(IV) is generated by abstraction of a proton from a second molecule of the carbonyl compound by a strong base. The very fact that the carbanion (IV) can be formed initially requires some comment, for most C—H bonds do not respond to basic attack so readily.

Our interpretation is again based upon the proposed relationship between stability and ease of formation (p. 64). Because of the presence of the adjacent C=O, IV is no ordinary carbanion. Examination of the bonding arrangement makes it clear that the electrons in the carbanion orbital can overlap with the π-electrons in the C=O, resulting in some of the negative charge being shifted onto the highly electronegative oxygen atom.

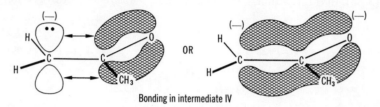

Bonding in intermediate IV

The consequent increased stability is reflected in the relative ease with which carbanions can be formed in positions adjacent to carbonyl groups. The only compounds in which carbon is the negative end of a polar bond are those in which carbon is attached directly to a metallic element. The most familiar of such "organometallic" reagents is the Grignard reagent, which contains a carbon–magnesium bond. Equation (5–37) shows a typical reaction in which the highly nucleo-

$$CH_3\overset{\delta-}{C}H_2—\overset{\delta+}{M}gBr + CH_3\overset{O}{\overset{\|}{C}}CH_3 \longrightarrow CH_3—\overset{O^-MgBr^+}{\underset{CH_2CH_3}{\overset{|}{C}}}—CH_3 \xrightarrow{+H_2O}$$

$$CH_3—\overset{OH}{\underset{CH_2CH_3}{\overset{|}{C}}}—CH_3 + Mg(OH)Br \quad (5\text{–}37)$$

philic carbon of a Grignard reagent, CH_3CH_2MgBr, adds to the carbonyl group of acetone. It will be seen in Chapter 6 that reactions (5–36) and (5–37) are of particular significance in synthesis, because they result in the formation of new C—C bonds. A knowledge of the mechanism of reactions like (5–36) has been helpful in understanding the manner in which many carbon chains are built up in biological systems, for the process is closely related to reactions of this type. These and other reactions of carbonyl compounds are discussed more fully in reference (2).

ELIMINATION REACTIONS

Just as addition reactions occur at unsaturated centers, so elimination reactions generally produce unsaturated centers by the removal of groups from two adjacent carbon atoms. The bonds to the two groups eliminated may be broken either simultaneously or in two separate steps. One familiar example of the former is outlined in equation (5–38). In this reaction, a strong base (OH^-) abstracts a hydrogen ion

$$CH_3-\overset{Br}{\underset{H}{C^2}}-\overset{H}{\underset{(H}{C^1}}-H \longrightarrow \overset{CH_3}{\underset{H}{}}C=C\overset{H}{\underset{H}{}} + Br^- + H_2O \qquad (5\text{–}38)$$

$$:\ddot{O}-H^-$$

from carbon atom number 1, in a typical bond-breaking process analogous to reaction (5–8). *Simultaneously*, the carbon–bromine bond on carbon atom number 2 breaks, the leaving bromide ion taking the electron pair. As the two bonds break, the developing electron pair on C-1 and vacant orbital on C-2 merge to form the π-bond of the product alkene.

The same overall process represented by (5–38), namely the loss of H—Br (or analogous groups) to form an alkene, also occurs by the two-step process outlined in (5–39). The bond-breaking processes in (5–39) are essentially the same as in (5–38), but the timing is different.

$$CH_3-\overset{Br}{\underset{H}{C}}-\overset{H}{\underset{H}{C}}-H \longrightarrow Br^- + \overset{CH_3}{\underset{H}{}}\overset{+}{C}-\overset{H}{\underset{H}{C}}-H$$

$$\downarrow \overset{..}{O} \overset{H}{\diagdown}{}^{H}$$

$$\overset{CH_3}{\underset{H}{}}C=C\overset{H}{\underset{H}{}} + H_3O^+ \qquad (5\text{–}39)$$

---

(2) C. D. Gutsche, *Chemistry of Carbonyl Compounds*, Prentice-Hall, Inc., Englewood Cliffs, N.J., 1967.

Although breakage of the C—Br bond in (5–39) appears to be an unassisted process, there is little doubt that hydrogen bonding from the solvent helps remove Br^- in both (5–38) and (5–39). Which mechanism accounts for the elimination of H—Br in a particular reaction will depend upon both the reaction conditions, e.g., the strength of the base (or nucleophile) present, and the structure of the reactant. The latter will affect the stability and therefore, presumably, the ease of formation of the carbonium ion intermediate of (5–39).

The perceptive reader may have recognized that the sequence of bond-breaking steps in (5–39) is precisely the reverse of the bond-forming steps in the addition of H—Br to propylene described above [equation (5–26)]. (A direct comparison of the two reactions is suggested.) Additions to C—O double bonds are often similarly reversible, and the "back reactions" shown in equations (5–34) and (5–35) are elimination reactions initiated by electrophilic and nucleophilic attack, respectively.

SUBSTITUTION REACTIONS

By far the largest class of organic reactions, substitution reactions are also the most versatile in terms of the variety of mechanisms by which they may occur. They may be conveniently grouped according to the timing of the breaking of the bond to the leaving group and formation of the new bond to the entering group. Either of these processes may occur first, or, as in our first example, they may occur simultaneously.

Simultaneous Bond-breaking and Bond-formation

We have seen that bonds such as those between a carbon and a halogen atom, which are significantly polar, may cleave without a great deal of assistance to form a carbonium ion [equation (5–39)]. This occurs readily only if the carbonium ion formed is a relatively stable one, stabilized by the presence of three alkyl groups on the positive carbon, for example. In one of the most important types of substitution reactions, a nucleophile assists in breaking the C—X bond by pushing on the carbon atom from the side opposite the leaving X^-. The process is illustrated in equation (5–40) for the nucleophile OH^-. The structure in brackets in (5–40) is *not* an intermediate, i.e., it does

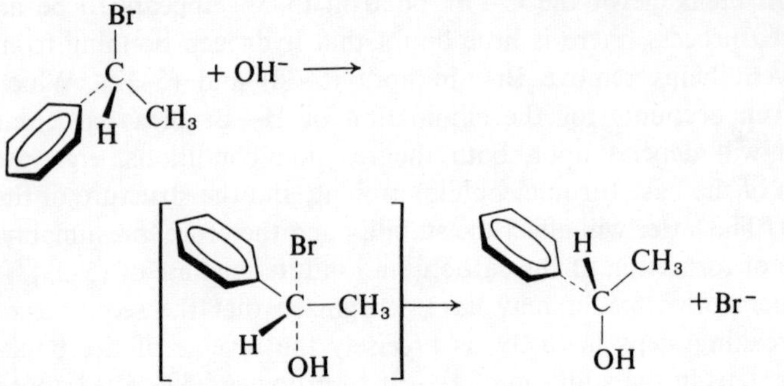

$$(5\text{-}40)$$

$$S_N2 \text{ Substitution}$$

not exist for a significant length of time, but represents a configuration through which the reactants pass on the way to the products. A distinctive feature of nucleophilic substitution reactions occurring by this mechanism, commonly designated the S_N2 mechanism, is its stereochemistry. If the substrate is optically active (cf. p. 18) due to asymmetry at the carbon atom being attacked, as it is in our example (5–40), then the product will also be optically active, but the configuration of the carbon atom is inverted, turned inside out like an umbrella on a windy day. Since there is no intermediate in the S_N2 mechanism, the ease with which the reaction takes place depends primarily upon the polarity and strength of the bond to the leaving group and the ease with which the entering group can approach the carbon atom. For the latter reason, S_N2 reactions occur primarily with "unhindered" substrates, i.e., compounds with a minimum number of bulky groups attached to the carbon atom being attacked. A large number of reactions involving many different leaving groups and nucleophiles, occur by this mechanism. Several such reactions are shown in Table 6–1 (e.g., equations 10, 16, 27, 32, 44). A recent review of this type of reaction [reference (3)] describes many examples of its occurrence among both organic and inorganic compounds.

Bond-breaking Preceding Bond-formation

Other substitution reactions at saturated carbon atoms require that the bond to the leaving group be broken *prior* to the formation of the new bond to the entering group. This necessitates a mechanism con-

---

[3] J. O. Edwards, *J. Chem. Educ.*, **45**, 386 (1968).

sisting of at least two steps and may involve either carbonium ion, carbanion, or radical intermediates.

Alkyl halides which are too hindered to undergo S_N2 substitution readily may produce the same type of products by a two-step mechanism involving carbonium ion intermediates. Indeed, the same substrate may be forced to react by either mechanism simply by variation of the reaction conditions. In reaction (5–41), the overall transformation is identical to that shown in reaction (5–40), but in the absence of the strong nucleophile (OH^-) a very different mechanism takes precedence.

$$Br^- + \quad \overset{+}{\underset{H}{C}}-CH_3 \xrightarrow{+H_2O} \quad \overset{OH}{\underset{}{CH}}-CH_3 + H^+ \quad (5\text{--}41)$$

S_N1 Substitution

Although it may produce a product with the same structure, the stereochemical result of this path, designated the S_N1 mechanism, is very different from that in the S_N2 reaction. The intermediate carbonium ion in an S_N1 reaction is planar, and when the entering nucleophile attacks, it is equally likely that it will approach from above or below this plane. Consequently, both optical isomers, or enantiomers, of the product are formed, in equal amounts; i.e., the product is a racemic mixture.

Substitution reactions involving carbanion intermediates depend upon generation of the carbanion in the same manner demonstrated in equation (5–36) for the addition of carbanions to carbonyl groups, namely by removal of a hydrogen ion by a strong base. Thus, many common representatives of this type of reaction involve substitution of a halogen for hydrogen on the carbon atom adjacent to a carbon–oxygen double bond, as in (5–42). The bond-forming step in (5–42)

$$CH_3\overset{O}{\overset{\|}{C}}CH_3 + OH^- \rightleftharpoons H_2O + CH_3-\overset{O}{\overset{\|}{C}}-\overset{-}{CH_2}$$

$$\xrightarrow{+Cl_2} CH_3-\overset{O}{\overset{\|}{C}}-CH_2-Cl + Cl^- \quad (5\text{--}42)$$

79

was presented in equation (5–14) as an example of the attack of the electrophile Cl_2 upon a carbanion.

Perhaps the most important reactions in which bond-breaking precedes bond-formation are the radical substitution reactions— important if for no other reason than that nearly all of the useful reactions of alkanes fall in this category. The chlorination of methane, equation (5–43), is typical of this group of reactions, and the sequence of steps which accounts for the formation of methyl chloride is shown in equations (5–44) to (5–47). Note that this set of reactions con-

$$CH_4 + Cl_2 \rightarrow \quad CH_3—Cl \quad + HCl \qquad (5–43)$$
$$\text{Methyl chloride}$$
$$Cl_2 \rightarrow 2Cl· \qquad (5–44)$$
$$Cl· + CH_4 \rightarrow CH_3· + H—Cl \qquad (5–45)$$
$$CH_3· + Cl—Cl \rightarrow CH_3—Cl + Cl· \qquad (5–46)$$
$$CH_3· + CH_3· \rightarrow CH_3 —CH_3 \qquad (5–47)$$

stitutes a *chain* reaction, very comparable to the radical addition reaction in equations (5–28) to (5–31). The key reactions in the cycle are (5–45) and (5–46), for every time a chlorine atom is consumed in (5–45), another chlorine atom is subsequently produced by reaction (5–46), and this chlorine atom starts the (5–45), (5–46) cycle again. As we saw before, reaction (5–47) occurs only infrequently, so that a single chlorine atom formed in (5–44) may initiate a cycle which produces hundreds of CH_3—Cl molecules before the radical is destroyed by a termination step. An additional example of the same type of reaction, equation (5–48) also illustrates the effect of structure upon the ease with which hydrogen atoms can be abstracted in this reaction. There are four types of hydrogen atoms which might be replaced in this substrate: the hydrogens on the aromatic ring (not

$$CH_3—\bigcirc—CH_2—CH_3 + Br_2 \longrightarrow$$

$$CH_3—\bigcirc—\overset{\overset{\displaystyle Br}{|}}{CH}—CH_3 + HBr \qquad (5–48)$$

shown in the formula), the hydrogen of the CH_3 on the ring, the CH_2 hydrogens, and the second CH_3 hydrogens. Why is a hydrogen on the CH_2 the one which is replaced? The principle that the stability of the intermediate should determine its ease of formation is again applicable, as it has been shown that radicals are stabilized both by adjacent alkyl groups and aromatic rings. Removal of one of the CH_2 hydrogens in (5–48) leads to an intermediate with the structure shown in V–a, stabilized by a CH_3 group and the aromatic ring. Removal of a hydrogen from either CH_3 group would have produced a radical

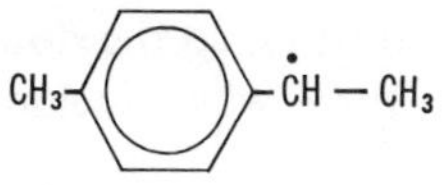

V'–a 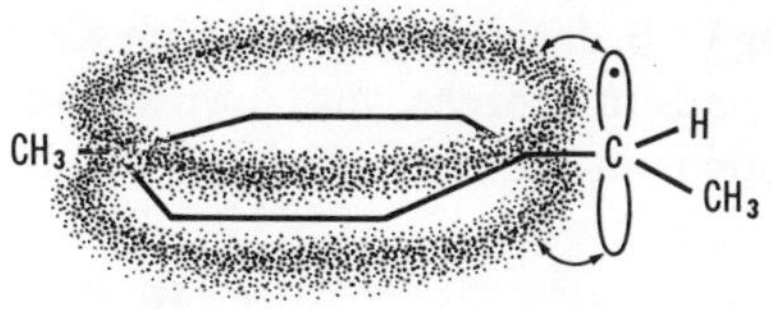   V–b

stabilized by only one of these factors. The stabilizing effect of the adjacent aromatic ring is a result of interaction of the orbital containing the odd electron with the π-orbitals of the aromatic ring, represented schematically in V–b.

Bond-formation Preceding Bond-breaking

If the new bond in a substitution reaction is to be formed before the old bond is broken, then the reaction must take place at an unsaturated center, just as addition reactions do. There are important examples of both electrophilic and nucleophilic reactions in this category, and both will be discussed at some length.

In the discussion of electrophilic addition to alkenes, it was stressed that aromatic rings do not undergo such addition reactions, because they would destroy the stable, aromatic ring. Aromatic rings do react with electrophilic reagents, however, including many of the reagents which attack the alkenes. Following the initial electrophilic attack, the aromatics expel a hydrogen ion, H^+, thus regenerating the aromatic ring. The result is a substitution reaction, as shown in equation (5–49) for the reaction of benzene with bromine. The first step can be seen to

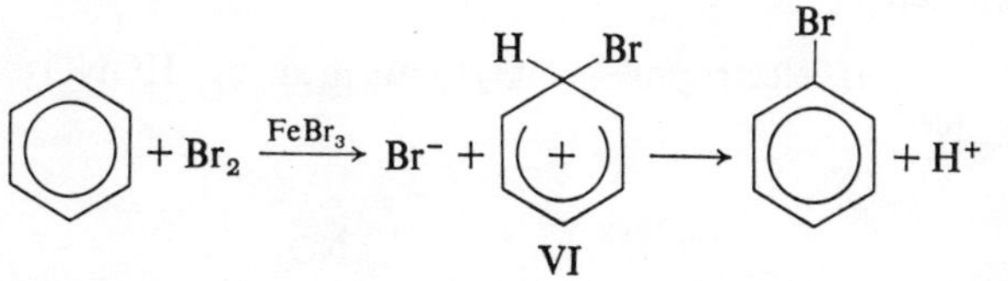

be virtually identical to the first step in the addition of bromine to an alkene [equation (5–23)], although the reaction of benzene requires assistance by a catalyst such as $FeBr_3$ or $AlBr_3$. The second step in reaction (5–49) is analogous to the loss of H^+ from other carbonium

81

ions, as exemplified in the elimination of H—Br [equation (5–39)]. The intermediate represented as VI in equation (5–49) requires some discussion. If the first step in this reaction is rewritten in terms of Kekulé structures for benzene, intermediate VI appears as either VI-a or VI-b, depending upon which Kekulé form is used. Just as the double bonds in benzene can be written in either of two ways, so the double bonds in the carbonium ion can be written in three ways, including

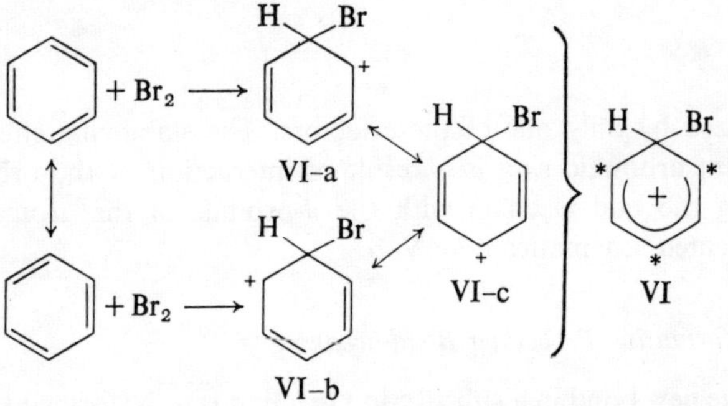

VI-a and VI-b, plus the additional structure VI-c. In order to emphasize the fact that the actual structure of the carbonium ion represents a compromise, or hybrid, between structures VI-a, VI-b, and VI-c, it is often represented simply as VI. It must be remembered, however, that the positive charge is distributed on three of the carbon atoms of the ring, namely the carbon atoms *ortho-* and *para-* to the attacking group, as indicated by the asterisks in VI.

The more common aromatic electrophilic substitution reactions, in addition to bromination (and chlorination), are described in the following list, which shows both the overall reaction and the nature of the electrophilic species which actually attacks the ring in the bond-forming step.

1. *Nitration:* electrophile, NO_2^+, formed by $HONO_2 + H^+ \rightarrow H_2O + NO_2^+$

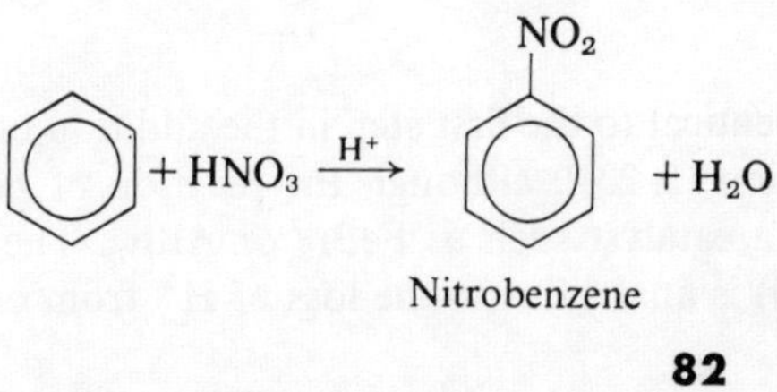

Nitrobenzene

2. *Sulfonation:* electrophile, SO_3, formed from $H_2SO_4 \rightarrow H_2O + SO_3$

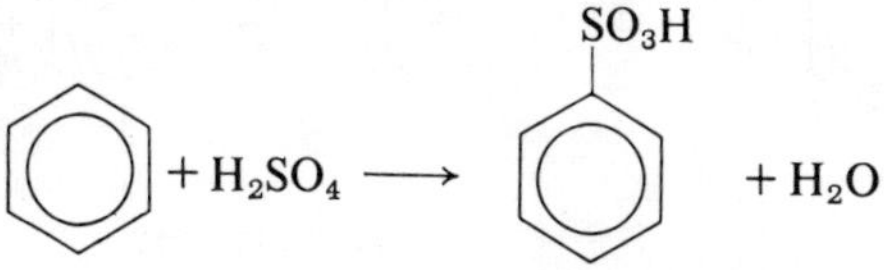

Benzenesulfonic
acid

3. *Alkylation:* electrophile, carbonium ion, formed from alkyl halide by $R{-}Cl + AlCl_3 \rightarrow R^+ + AlCl_4^-$

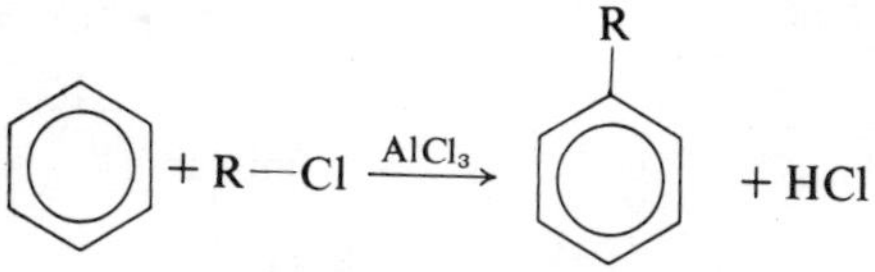

Alkyl benzene

4. *Acylation:* electrophile, acyl carbonium ion, formed from

$$R{-}\overset{\overset{\displaystyle O}{\|}}{C}{-}Cl + AlCl_3 \rightarrow R{-}\overset{\overset{\displaystyle O}{\|}}{C}{}^+ + AlCl_4^-$$

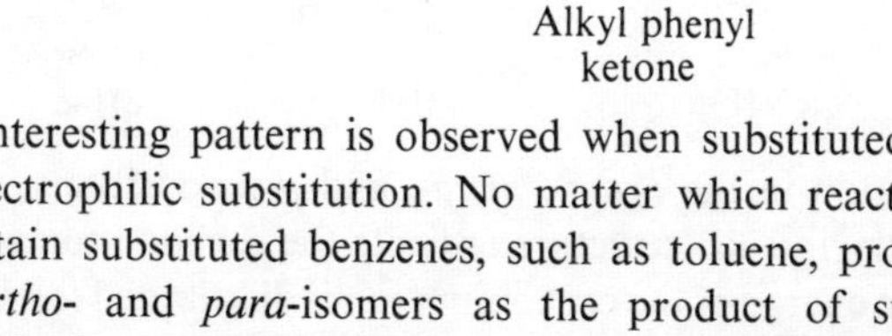

Alkyl phenyl
ketone

A very interesting pattern is observed when substituted benzenes undergo electrophilic substitution. No matter which reaction is employed, certain substituted benzenes, such as toluene, produce mixtures of *ortho-* and *para-*isomers as the product of substitution [equations (5–50) and (5–51)]. Others, such as nitrobenzene, produce *meta-*isomers as the major products, again regardless of the particular reaction [equation (5–52)]. Other substituents which, like —CH$_3$, are *ortho–para directing* include —OH, —NH$_2$, and the halogens, while among the common *meta directing* groups are —NO$_2$, —COOH, and —COR (ketone). An explanation of this phenomenon can be given in terms of the stability of the possible intermediates, again assuming the

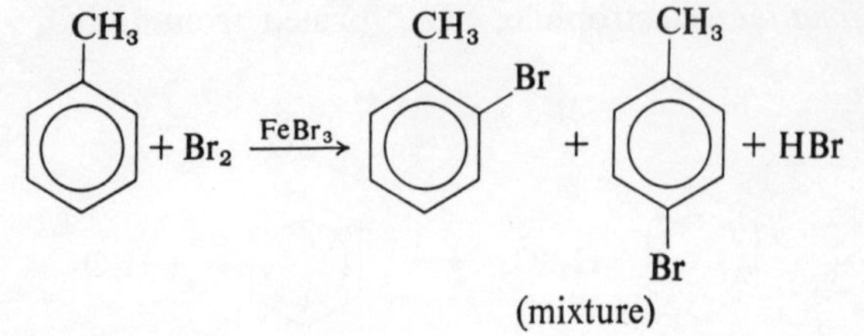

$$(5-50)$$

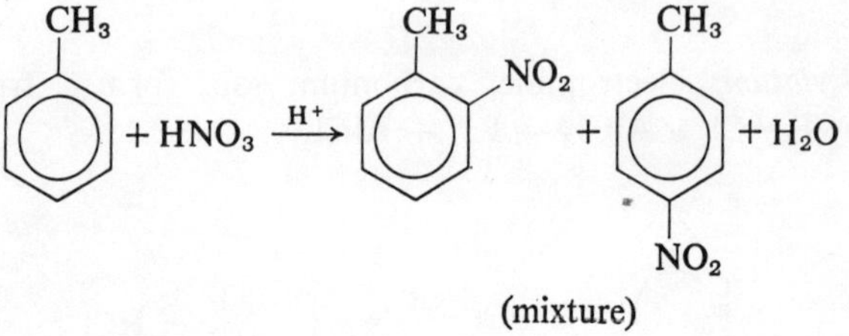

(mixture)

$$(5-51)$$

(mixture)

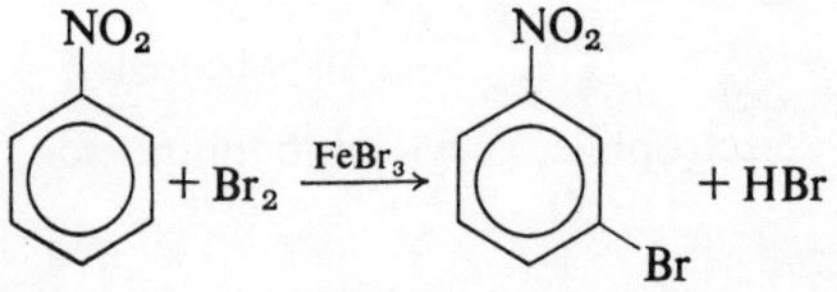

$$(5-52)$$

most stable to be most easily formed. In the bromination of toluene, three intermediates are conceivable, VII-a, VII-b, and VII-c, leading

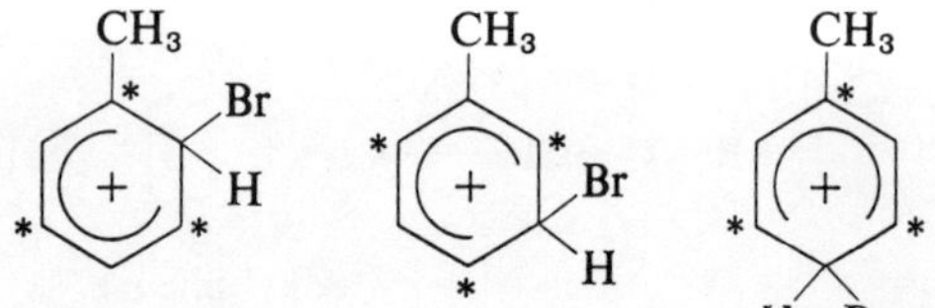

to substitution in the *ortho-*, *meta-*, and *para*-positions, respectively. The asterisks in each structure indicate the carbon atoms upon which the positive charge of the carbonium ion is distributed (*ortho-* and *para*- to the point of attack.) As mentioned earlier, alkyl groups help to stabilize carbonium ions, and the effect of the methyl group will be greater in VII-a and VII-c, where the positive charge resides partially upon the carbon atom attached to the —CH_3, than in VII-b, where the positive charge is one carbon atom removed from the —CH_3. We thus predict greater stability and easier formation of VII-a and VII-c than of VII-b, leading to products substituted in the *ortho-* and *para*-

positions. In general, *ortho–para* directing substituents are those which can help to stabilize the intermediate carbonium ion, and they thus make the aromatic ring more reactive, as well as controlling the pattern of substitution. Since the nitro group, $-NO_2$, is highly electronegative, it will have an effect opposite to that of an alkyl group. That is, the nitro group concentrates positive charge upon the ring, thus destabilizing the carbonium ion and making the ring less reactive than benzene itself. It will be *least* effective, however, in slowing down substitution at the *meta*-position, since with substitution at that position the positive charge stays further away from the deleterious $-NO_2$ than when substitution occurs at either the *ortho*- or *para*-position. Structures VIII-a and VIII-c show the unfavorable relationship between the $-NO_2$ and the positive charge, the interaction being less severe in VIII-b.

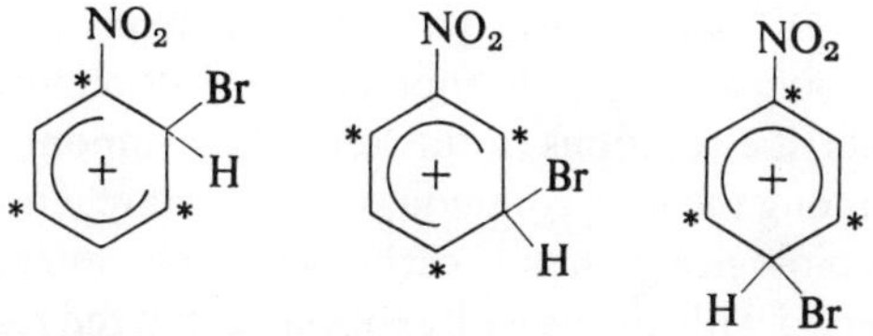

| VIII–a | VIII–b | VIII–c |

Aromatic halides are susceptible to nucleophilic attack by a mechanism very similar to that of electrophilic substitution, as illustrated in equation (5–53). The reaction requires extreme conditions (ca. 400°), however, and does not possess great generality. It is possible

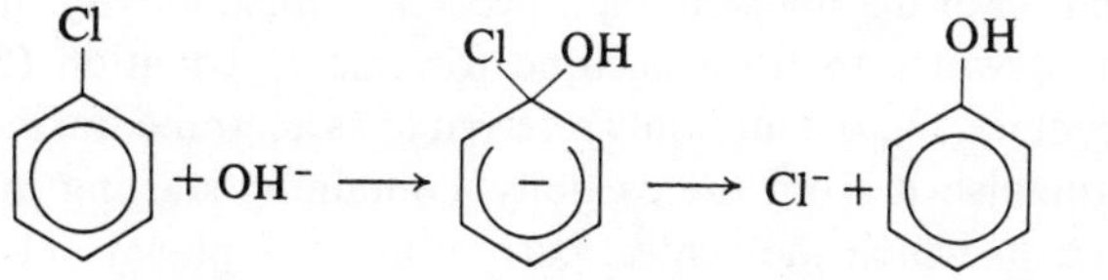

$$(5–53)$$

to increase the stability of the intermediate carbanion by placing substituents on the ring which stabilize negative charge, and the reaction may then go quite readily, as is the case with reaction (5–54). For a more detailed account of aromatic substitution reactions, consult references (4) and (5).

---

[4] H. Duewell, *J. Chem. Educ.*, **43**, 138 (1966).
[5] L. Stock, *Aromatic Substitution Reactions*, Prentice-Hall, Inc., Englewood Cliffs, N.J., 1968.

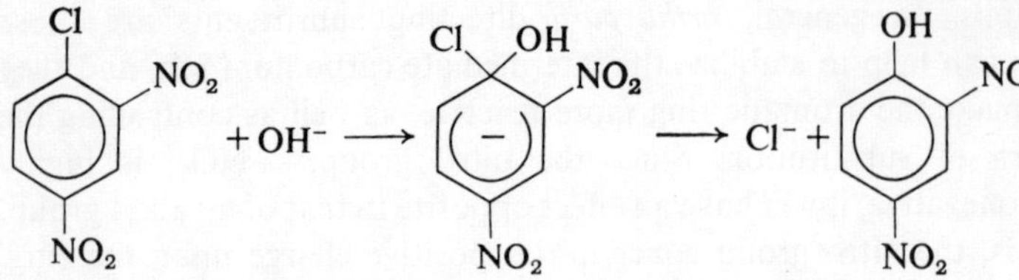

$$\text{(5-54)}$$

The susceptibility of carbonyl (C=O) groups to nucleophilic attack has already been documented in connection with addition reactions (p. 74). If the carbonyl group is attached to a highly electronegative substituent, nucleophilic addition to the carbonyl group may be followed by loss of this substituent group, the combination comprising a substitution reaction at the carbonyl group. The carboxylic acids and their derivatives—acid chlorides, esters, and amides—constitute a family of compounds in which the carbonyl group is attached to —OH, —Cl, —OR, and —NH$_2$, respectively, all of which are capable of acting as leaving groups. Nucleophilic substitution reactions are the prime characteristic reactions in this series of compounds, and many of them are among the very common, widespread reactions of organic chemistry. In biological systems, carboxylic acids, esters, and amides are interconverted with great ease by enzyme-catalyzed reactions of this type.

The reaction of an ester with aqueous sodium hydroxide [equation (5–55)] is typical, and involves steps which have been described previously. The first half of the reaction is an addition of water to the carbonyl group and results from initial attack by OH$^-$ [compare equation (5–34)]. The second half of the reaction amounts to the elimination of methyl alcohol, a process quite analogous to the elimination of water to form acetone [reverse of equation (5–34)]. The intermediate, IX, is commonly referred to as a tetrahedral intermediate, to distinguish it from the carbonyl-containing starting material and product, in which the central carbon atom is planar. The following

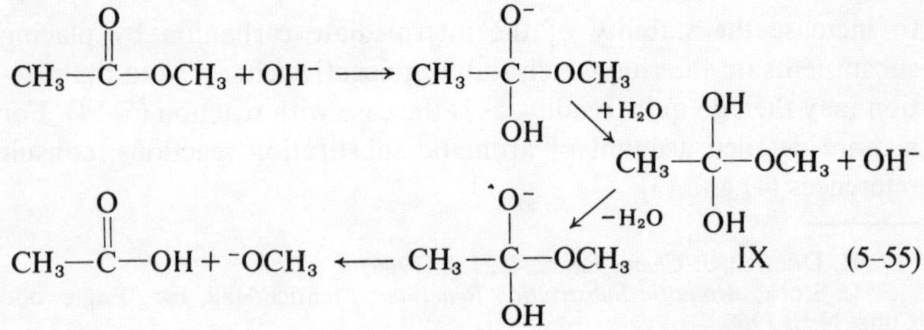

$$\text{(5-55)}$$

Conclusion

list should emphasize both the versatility of nucleophilic substitution reactions among carboxylic acid derivatives and the similarity of the mechanisms by which they take place. An excellent review of this type of reaction, reference (6), is worthy of the reader's attention.

Name of Reaction	Reactants	Tetrahedral Intermediate	Products
Hydrolysis:	$R-\overset{O}{\overset{\|}{C}}-Cl + OH^- \rightarrow$	$R-\overset{O^-}{\underset{OH}{\overset{\|}{C}}}-Cl \rightarrow$	$R-\overset{O}{\overset{\|}{C}}-OH + Cl^-$
Hydrolysis*: Esterification†:	$R-\overset{O}{\overset{\|}{C}}-OCH_3 + H_2O \rightleftharpoons$	$R-\overset{OH}{\underset{OH}{\overset{\|}{C}}}-OCH_3 \rightleftharpoons$	$R-\overset{O}{\overset{\|}{C}}-OH + CH_3OH$
Ammonolysis*: Alcoholysis†:	$R-\overset{O}{\overset{\|}{C}}-OCH_3 + NH_3 \rightleftharpoons$	$R-\overset{OH}{\underset{NH_2}{\overset{\|}{C}}}-OCH_3 \rightleftharpoons$	$R-\overset{O}{\overset{\|}{C}}-NH_2 + CH_3OH$
Ammonolysis*: Hydrolysis†:	$R-\overset{O}{\overset{\|}{C}}-OH + NH_3 \rightleftharpoons$	$R-\overset{OH}{\underset{NH_2}{\overset{\|}{C}}}-OH \rightleftharpoons$	$R-\overset{O}{\overset{\|}{C}}-NH_2 + H_2O$

* Name refers to forward reaction, as written.
† Name refers to reverse reaction, as written.

CONCLUSION

The reactions discussed in this chapter are but a few of those which are important to an organic chemist. They are representative of many, although certainly not all, of the types of reactions which commonly occur among organic compounds. The attempt has been made to approach these reactions in a manner consistent with the way in which the modern organic chemist thinks about them. An understanding of *how* reactions take place, as well as *what* reactions take place, serves as a guide to increased control over the course which reactions take and to the development of new reactions, patterned upon the mechanisms of those already known. Our discussion of organic reactions continues in the next chapter, as we see how the synthetic chemist deploys his arsenal of reactions in his attempt to prepare molecules of the desired structure.

[6] R. V. Cash, *J. Chem. Educ.*, **41**, 108 (1964).

C H A P T E R **6**

Organic Synthesis

Synthesis has sometimes been described as the cornerstone of organic chemistry. Even today, when much of the research emphasis is directed toward understanding reactions and their mechanisms, synthesis still occupies a position of importance in the discipline of organic chemistry. Let us look first at some of the reasons for the fact that the synthesis of organic compounds lies at the heart of the science.

REASONS FOR SYNTHESIS

In Chapter 4 we learned that the synthesis of an organic compound by an unambiguous route constitutes the final step in the confirmation of a tentatively assigned structure. Even though the use of such analytical tools as NMR spectroscopy frequently eliminates the necessity for confirmatory synthesis, it is still customary to supplement instrumental analysis by synthesis.

Because the biological properties of molecules can often be roughly correlated with their chemical structures, much time and attention has been devoted to the synthesis of compounds having potential biological activity. The antibiotic penicillin G was shown by X-ray diffraction analysis to have the structure given on page 89. Almost twenty years later this antibiotic was synthesized by J. C. Sheehan at Massachusetts Institute of Technology. Many such penicillin derivatives differing from penicillin G in having a different R group in place of the benzyl ($C_6H_5CH_2$—) group have now been synthesized. Some of these have

88

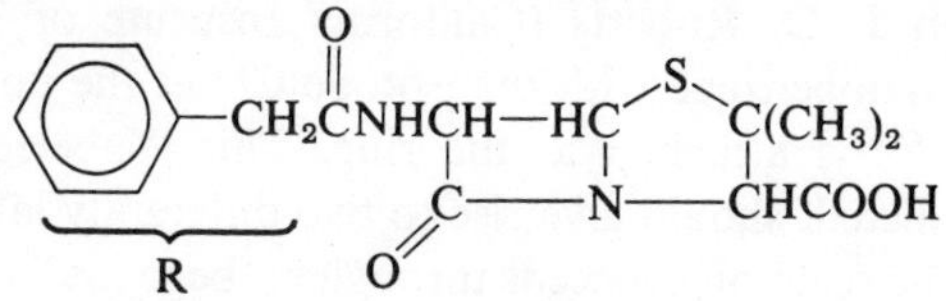

greater potency than the natural penicillins, which is of special significance since microorganisms attacked by the penicillins have become more resistant to the natural antibiotics over a period of years.

Molecules with special structural characteristics may be synthesized for the purpose of obtaining information which will confirm or refute theoretical postulations and predictions developed on the basis of known structural theory. Current molecular orbital theory predicts that a compound having aromatic characteristics (see Chapter 2) should possess a planar ring containing $(4n + 2)$ π-electrons where n equals a whole number. Shown below are the structural formulas of three compounds, which were synthesized for the purpose of testing the validity of this prediction.

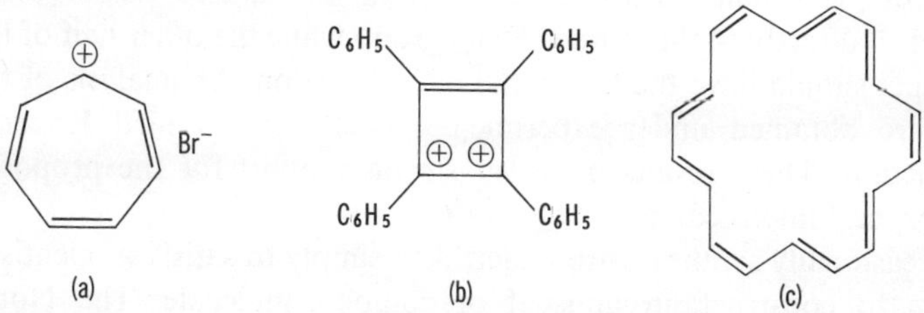

Like benzene, tropylium bromide (a) has six π-electrons but has seven carbon atoms in the ring. In the tetraphenylcyclobutenyl dication (b) we have a structure with a four-membered ring having just two π-electrons. For this compound n is 0 and the number of π-electrons is therefore 2. Compound (c) which fits the $4n + 2$ rule for $n = 4$ is known as [18]annulene.

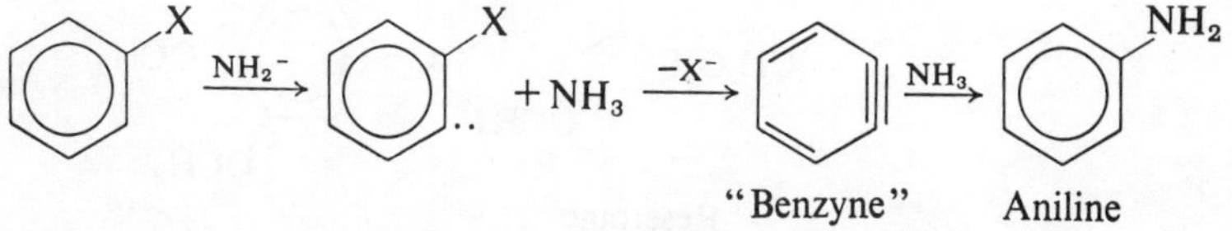

A synthesis may be executed for the purpose of studying the mechanism of a reaction. The reaction of halobenzenes with the strong base KNH_2 in liquid NH_3 was postulated to occur by way of a "benzyne" intermediate, as indicated in the sequence below. To test this prediction J. D. Roberts (California Institute of Technology) synthesized a halobenzene with the isotope C^{14} at the position where the halogen (X) is attached to the ring. This "labeled" aromatic halide, he predicted, should give rise to two differently labeled aniline derivatives if the reaction proceeds through a "benzyne" intermediate.

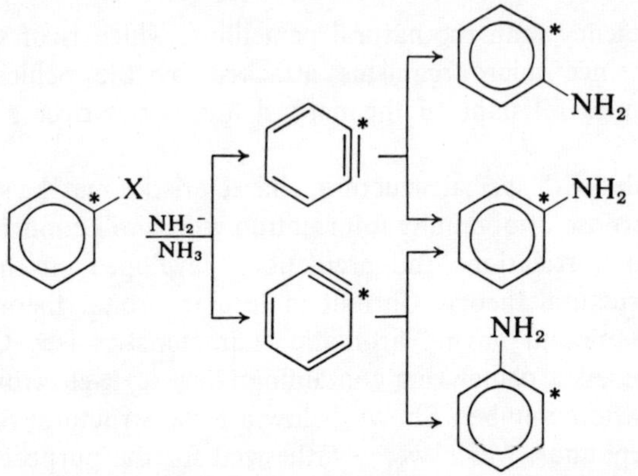

Half of the aniline formed should contain the labeled carbon atom attached directly to the amino (NH_2) group while the other half of the product should have the C^{14} in the ortho position. An analysis of the mixture obtained under experimental conditions verified Roberts' prediction. These results provided strong support for the proposed "benzyne" intermediate.

Occasionally syntheses are undertaken simply to satisfy a scientist's desire to construct an unusual or complex molecule. The Nobel laureate R. B. Woodward (Harvard) reported in 1958 the synthesis of reserpine, an alkaloid used for the treatment of some mental disorders and for the reduction of hypertension. In 1960 he described a procedure for the preparation of chlorophyll-a. The complexity of these natural products is evident in the following formulas:

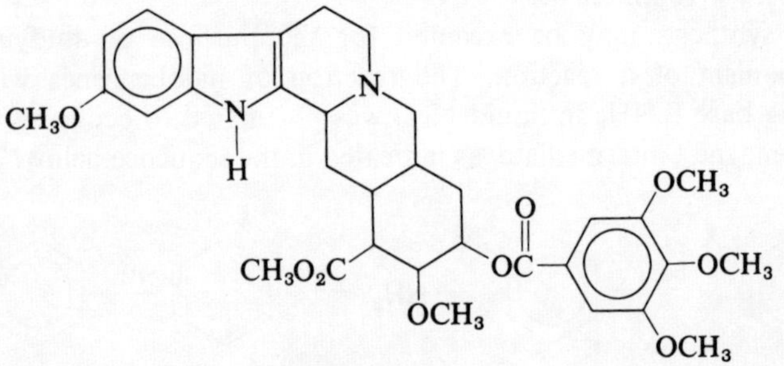

Reserpine

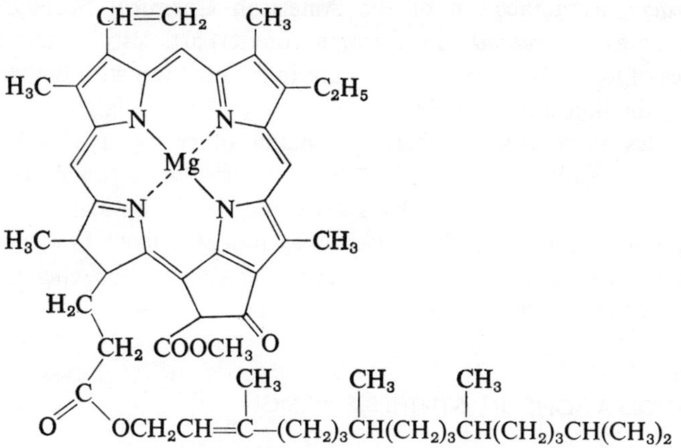

$$CH{=}CH_2 \quad CH_3$$

$$H_3C \qquad\qquad\qquad C_2H_5$$

$$N \qquad N$$

$$Mg$$

$$N \qquad N$$

$$H_3C \qquad\qquad\qquad CH_3$$

$$H_2C$$

$$CH_2 \quad COOCH_3 \quad O$$

$$CH_3 \qquad CH_3 \qquad CH_3$$

$$O \qquad OCH_2CH{=}C{-}(CH_2)_3CH(CH_2)_3CH(CH_2)_3CH(CH_3)_2$$

Chlorophyll—a

Undoubtedly the challenge of synthesizing molecules of this complexity was a motive (though certainly not the only one) for undertaking the syntheses.

THE CHEMICAL LITERATURE

Fortunately, the organic chemist, in designing a synthesis, may draw upon the experience of many other chemists. In the chemical literature there is much information from which he may obtain assistance. Information about a compound which may be sought includes molecular formula, structural formula (if known), physical properties, chemical properties, methods of preparation and isolation, and analytical data. These sources of information are available in any reputable science library. In recent years information retrieval has become an increasingly crucial problem because of the enormous quantity of published research. Computers and data processing machines are currently being used to provide the necessary title, author, subject, and formula indices to aid the chemist in his literature searching.

In addition to organic chemistry texts and laboratory manuals there are a number of standard reference books which are extremely useful to synthetic chemists. Abstracts of original journal articles may be found in abstracting journals. One of the most comprehensive of these sources is Beilstein's *Handbuch der Organischen Chemie*, a German treatise which covers the chemical literature through 1929. *Chemical*

Abstracts, a publication of the American Chemical Society, and *Chemisches Zentralblatt*, its German counterpart, also contain summaries of journal articles and are used in conjunction with Beilstein to survey the literature completely.

Besides these sources there are many other types of reference volumes—handbooks, encyclopedias of organic compounds, and books on special topics such as aromatic substitution, heterocyclic compounds, photochemical reactions and the like. For a more complete catalogue of the literature available to the chemist the interested reader may consult reference (1).

CONSIDERATIONS IN SYNTHESIS DESIGN

Having consulted the literature for whatever assistance might be obtained from the experience of others, the organic chemist next must combine his own training and ingenuity to consider possible routes toward the objective of his synthesis. A variety of approaches and a number of trial and error attempts are frequently required to complete a successful synthesis. Let us look at some of the criteria which must be considered and evaluated in the selection of a synthetic sequence.

One of the factors critical to the success of a synthesis is the availability of starting materials. In planning a synthesis it is customary to write the structural formula for the compound to be prepared and then, working backwards in a stepwise procedure, the possible alternatives for the formation of the necessary intermediates are examined. At every step reactions are selected which permit the desired compound to be made from a readily available raw material. Frequently "blind alleys" necessitate the use of other options. There emerges from this procedure a possible synthetic route attractive enough for a laboratory trial.

The cost of raw materials is an important concern, especially if the synthesis is to be used for commercial purposes. However, economic factors must always be weighed against expediency and practicality. As the number of intermediate steps is increased the yield of the final product is reduced proportionally. Reactions are chosen which promise the highest possible yield and for which there is a minimum number of side reactions. Hazardous reactions are avoided and

---

[1] D. J. Cram and G. S. Hammond, *Organic Chemistry*, 2nd Ed., McGraw-Hill Book Co., New York, N.Y., 1964.

reactions requiring complex or expensive equipment are rejected if such apparatus is unavailable. Some difficulties can not always be anticipated despite careful planning and occasionally a specific synthetic scheme must be abandoned after considerable work has been devoted to it.

On the following pages are tabulated some of the common reactions used by organic chemists in synthetic work. Some of these reactions will be used to illustrate the conception and implementation of a synthesis.

Table 6–1

Common Reactions Used in Preparative Organic Chemistry

Type of Compound
to be Synthesized   Reaction

Alkanes

1. $RCH{=}CHR + H_2 \xrightarrow{catalyst} RCH_2CH_2R$
2. $2\,RCH_2Br + 2\,Na \rightarrow RCH_2CH_2R + 2\,NaBr$
3. $RMgBr + H_2O \rightarrow R{-}H + MgBrOH$
4. $Ar{-}H + RX \xrightarrow{AlCl_3} Ar{-}R + HX$
5. $ArCR + 2\,H_2 \xrightarrow{catalyst} ArCH_2R + H_2O$
   $\quad \underset{O}{\|}$

Alkenes

6. $RCHOHCH_3 \xrightarrow{acid} RCH{=}CH_2 + H_2O$
7. $RCHBrCH_3 \xrightarrow{base} RCH{=}CH_2 + HBr$
8. $RC{\equiv}CR \xrightarrow[Pd]{H_2} RCH{=}CHR$

Alkynes

9. $RCHBrCHBrR \xrightarrow{base} RC{\equiv}CR + 2\,HBr$
10. $RC{\equiv}C^-Na^+ + RX \rightarrow RC{\equiv}CR + Na^+X^-$

Alcohols

11. $RCH{=}CH_2 + H_2O \xrightarrow{H^+} RCHCH_3$
    $\qquad\qquad\qquad\qquad\quad |$
    $\qquad\qquad\qquad\qquad\;\; OH$
12. $RCH{=}CH_2 \xrightarrow[2.\ H_2O_2]{1.\ B_2H_6} RCH_2CH_2OH$
13. $RMgX + CH_2{=}O \rightarrow RCH_2OMgX$
    $\qquad\qquad\qquad\qquad\quad \xrightarrow{H_2O} RCH_2OH$
14. $RMgX + R'CH{=}O \rightarrow RCHOMgX$
    $\qquad\qquad\qquad\qquad\qquad |$
    $\qquad\qquad\qquad\qquad\;\; R'$
    $\qquad\qquad\qquad\qquad\qquad\quad \xrightarrow{H_2O} RCHOH$
    $\qquad\qquad\qquad\qquad\qquad\qquad\qquad\quad |$
    $\qquad\qquad\qquad\qquad\qquad\qquad\qquad\; R'$

Alcohol (cont.) 15. $RMgX + R'C{=}O \rightarrow R'\underset{\underset{R''}{|}}{\overset{\overset{R}{|}}{C}}{-}OMgX$

$$\xrightarrow{H_2O} R'\underset{\underset{R''}{|}}{\overset{\overset{R}{|}}{C}}{-}OH$$

16. $RBr + OH^- \xrightarrow{H_2O} ROH + Br^-$

17. $RCH{=}O + H_2 \xrightarrow{catalyst} RCH_2OH$

18. $R_2C{=}O + H_2 \xrightarrow{catalyst} R_2CHOH$

19. $RCOOR' + 4\,[H] \rightarrow RCH_2OH + R'OH$

Aldehydes 20. $RCH_2OH \xrightarrow{Cu} RCH{=}O + H_2$

21. $RCOCl \xrightarrow[BaSO_4]{H_2,\,Pd} RCH{=}O + HCl$

Acids 22. $RCH_2OH \xrightarrow{(O)} RCH{=}O \xrightarrow{(O)} RCOOH$

23. $Ar{-}R \xrightarrow{(O)} ArCOOH + CO_2 + H_2O$

24. $RC{\equiv}N + 2\,H_2O \xrightarrow[OH^-]{H^+\,or} RCOOH + NH_3$

25. $RMgBr + CO_2 \rightarrow RCOOMgBr \xrightarrow{H_2O} RCOOH$

Amines 26. $RNO_2 + 3\,H_2 \xrightarrow{catalyst} RNH_2 + 2\,H_2O$

27. $RX + NH_3 \longrightarrow RNH_2 \xrightarrow{RX} R_2NH$
$$\xrightarrow{RX} R_3N$$

28. $RC{\equiv}N + 2\,H_2 \xrightarrow{catalyst} RCH_2NH_2$

29. $RCH{=}O + NH_3 + H_2 \rightarrow RCH_2NH_2 + H_2O$

30. $RCONH_2 \xrightarrow{OBr^-} RNH_2 + CO_2 + Br^-$

Ethers 31. $2\,ROH \xrightarrow{H^+} R{-}O{-}R + H_2O$

32. $RO^-Na^+ + R'Br \rightarrow R{-}O{-}R' + Na^+Br^-$

Epoxides 33. $RCH{=}CHR + R\underset{\underset{O}{\|}}{C}OOH \longrightarrow$

$$R\underset{\underset{O}{\diagdown\diagup}}{CH}{-}CHR + RCOOH$$

Ketones 34. $R_2CHOH \xrightarrow{(O)} R_2C{=}O + H_2O$

35. $Ar{-}H + RCOCl \xrightarrow{AlCl_3} Ar{-}\underset{\underset{O}{\|}}{C}{-}R + HCl$

36. $Ar{-}H + R\underset{\underset{O}{\diagdown}}{C}{=}O \xrightarrow{AlCl_3} Ar{-}\underset{\underset{O}{\|}}{C}{-}R + RCOOH$
$$\underset{\underset{RC{=}O}{\diagup}}{}$$

Ketones (cont.)	37. $RCOCl + R'CdCl \rightarrow R-\underset{\underset{O}{\|}}{C}-R' + CdCl_2$
Acid chlorides	38. $RCOOH + SOCl_2 \rightarrow RCOCl + SO_2 + HCl$
	39. $RCOOH + PCl_5 \rightarrow RCOCl + HCl + POCl_3$
Acid anhydrides	40. $RCOCl + RCOOH$

$$\xrightarrow{\text{pyridine}} R-\underset{\underset{O}{\|}}{C}-O-\underset{\underset{O}{\|}}{C}-R + HCl$$

Acid amides	41. $RCOCl + 2 NH_3 \rightarrow RCONH_2 + NH_4Cl$
	42. $R-\underset{\underset{O}{\|}}{C}-O-\underset{\underset{O}{\|}}{C}-R + 2 NH_3$ $\longrightarrow$

$$RCONH_2 + RCOONH_4$$

	43. $RCOONH_4 \xrightarrow{\Delta} RCONH_2 + H_2O$
Nitriles	44. $RBr + CN^- \rightarrow R-CN + Br^-$
	45. $Ar-N\equiv N^+X^- + CN^-$

$$\xrightarrow{\text{CuCN}} ArCN + N_2 + X^-$$

Phenols	46. $ArSO_3^-Na^+ + NaOH \longrightarrow ArO^-Na^+$

$$\xrightarrow{H^+} ArOH$$

	47. $Ar-N\equiv N^+X^- + H_2O \rightarrow Ar-OH + N_2 + X^-$
Nitro-compounds	48. $Ar-H + HNO_3 \xrightarrow{H_2SO_4} Ar-NO_2 + H_2O$
Esters	49. $ROH + R'COOH \xrightarrow{H^+} R'COOR + H_2O$
	50. $RCOCl + R'OH \rightarrow RCOOR' + HCl$
	51. $R-\underset{\underset{O}{\|}}{C}-O-\underset{\underset{O}{\|}}{C}-R + R'OH \longrightarrow$

$$RCOOR' + RCOOH$$

Halides	52. $ROH + HX \rightarrow RX + H_2O$
	53. $3 ROH + PX_3 \rightarrow 3 RX + H_3PO_3$
	54. $RCH=CH_2 + HX \rightarrow RCHXCH_3$
	55. $RCH=CH_2 + HBr \xrightarrow{\text{peroxide}} RCH_2CH_2Br$
	56. $ArN\equiv N^+ + CuCl(Br)$

$$\rightarrow ArCl(Br) + N_2 + Cu^+$$

	57. $ArN\equiv N^+BF_4^- \xrightarrow{\Delta} Ar-F + N_2 + BF_3$
	58. $RCH=CHR + X_2 \rightarrow RCHXCHXR$
	59. $RCH=CH_2 + X_2 + H_2O$

$$\rightarrow RCHOHCH_2X + HX$$

	60. $Ar-H + Cl_2(Br_2) \xrightarrow{FeCl_3} Ar-Cl(Br) + HCl(Br)$

95

The equations in Table 6–1 represent reactions which, for the most part, do not lengthen the carbon chain in a molecule (exceptions are equations 2, 4, 10, 13, 14, 15, 25, 35, 36, 37, 44, and 45). Rather, they are reactions which involve the conversion of one functional group to another. In equation 1 the group —CH=CH is converted to —CH$_2$CH$_2$; in equation 3 —MgBr is replaced by —H; in equation 5 —COR is reduced to —CH$_2$R. To construct the carbon skeleton for larger molecules it is often necessary to build the desired skeleton from smaller carbon units through reactions uniting carbon to carbon. Some of these reactions are illustrated in the exceptions noted above. Table 6–2 lists other reactions which are especially useful in extending carbon chains.

Table 6–2

Reactions Commonly Used to Lengthen Carbon Chains

61. $2\ RCH_2CH{=}O \xrightarrow{\text{base}} RCH\overset{\overset{\displaystyle R}{|}}{C}H\underset{\underset{\displaystyle OH}{|}}{C}HCH{=}O$

62. $Ar{-}CH{=}O + CH_3\underset{\underset{\displaystyle O}{\|}}{C}R \xrightarrow{\text{base}} ArCH{=}CH\underset{\underset{\displaystyle O}{\|}}{C}R + H_2O$

63. $ArCH{=}O + CH_3{-}\underset{\underset{\displaystyle O}{\|}}{C}{-}O{-}\underset{\underset{\displaystyle O}{\|}}{C}{-}CH_3$
    $\xrightarrow{\text{base}} ArCH{=}CHCOOH + CH_3COOH$

64. $R{-}\underset{\underset{\displaystyle H(R)}{|}}{C}{=}O + BrZnCH_2COOC_2H_5 \xrightarrow{\text{2 steps}} R\overset{\overset{\displaystyle OH}{|}}{\underset{\underset{\displaystyle H(R)}{|}}{C}}CH_2COOC_2H_5$

65. $RMgX + \underset{\underset{\displaystyle O}{\diagdown\diagup}}{CH_2{-}CH_2} \longrightarrow RCH_2CH_2OMgX \xrightarrow{H_2O} RCH_2CH_2OH$

66. $RX + \underset{\underset{\displaystyle COOC_2H_5}{|}}{CH_2COOC_2H_5} \xrightarrow{\text{base}} \underset{\underset{\displaystyle COOC_2H_5}{|}}{RCHCOOC_2H_5}$

67. $RX + CH_3\underset{\underset{\displaystyle O}{\|}}{C}CH_2COOC_2H_5 \xrightarrow{\text{base}} CH_3\underset{\underset{\displaystyle O}{\|}}{C}{-}\underset{\underset{\displaystyle R}{|}}{C}HCOOC_2H_5$

68. $2\ RCH_2COOC_2H_5 \xrightarrow{\text{base}} RCH_2\underset{\underset{\displaystyle O}{\|}}{C}{-}\underset{\underset{\displaystyle R}{|}}{C}HCOOC_2H_5 + C_2H_5OH$

96

Let us now make use of some of the principles and reactions presented on the preceding pages in an attempt to solve an actual synthesis problem—the synthesis of $C_6H_5CH_2CH_2CH_2OH$, 3-phenyl-1-propanol. For purposes of illustration we shall assume that the compound is not commercially available in quantities sufficient for our needs.

Below are sketched some, though by no means all, of the possible routes to the synthesis of $C_6H_5CH_2CH_2CH_2OH$.

A. $\quad C_6H_5CH_2CH_2CH_2OH \xleftarrow[H_2O]{OH^- \ (16)} C_6H_5CH_2CH_2CH_2Br$

$\qquad\qquad\qquad\qquad\qquad\qquad\qquad\qquad$ HBr (55) $\Big\uparrow$ peroxide

B. $\quad C_6H_5CH_2CH_2CH_2OH \xleftarrow[2. \ H_2O_2]{1. \ B_2H_6 \ (12)} C_6H_5CH_2CH=CH_2$

$\qquad\qquad\qquad\qquad\qquad\qquad\qquad\qquad\qquad$ $\Big\uparrow$ HF (4)

$\qquad\qquad\qquad\qquad\qquad\qquad C_6H_6 + CH_2=CHCH_2Cl$

C. $\quad C_6H_5CH_2CH_2CH_2OH \xleftarrow{2[H] \ (17)} C_6H_5CH_2CH_2CHO$

$\qquad\qquad\qquad\qquad\qquad\qquad\qquad \uparrow \dfrac{H_2, \ Pd}{BaSO_4 \ (21)} C_6H_5CH_2CH_2COCl$

$\qquad\qquad\qquad\qquad\qquad\qquad\qquad\qquad (38) \Big\uparrow SOCl_2$

$\qquad C_6H_5CH-CHCOOH \xrightarrow[catalyst]{H_2(1)} C_6H_5CH_2CH_2COOH$

D. $C_6H_5CH_2CH_2CH_2OH \xleftarrow[H^+]{H_2O \ (65)} C_6H_5CH_2CH_2CH_2OMgX$

$\qquad\qquad\qquad\qquad\qquad\qquad (65) \Big\uparrow \overset{CH_2-CH_2}{\underset{O}{\diagdown\diagup}}$

$\qquad\qquad C_6H_5CH_2X \xrightarrow{Mg, \ ether} C_6H_5CH_2MgX$

E. $\quad C_6H_5CH_2CH_2CH_2OH \xleftarrow[cat.]{H_2(19)} C_6H_5CH_2CH_2COOC_2H_5$

$\qquad\qquad\qquad\qquad\qquad\qquad (49) \Big\uparrow \overset{H^+}{\underset{C_2H_5OH}{}}$

$\qquad C_6H_5CH=CHCOOH \xrightarrow[(1)]{H_2, \ Catalyst} C_6H_5CH_2CH_2COOH$

The last steps in Methods A through E represent five procedures for making primary alcohols as seen in Table 6–2. By working backwards, one step at a time, we eventually arrive at starting materials which we recognize as commercially available raw materials. Each of the intermediate steps is a well known reaction which the reader may find in Tables 6–1 and 6–2.

A closer examination of Methods A–E reveals that Method D has fewer experimental steps, a feature which makes this route especially attractive. Operationally, it involves the preparation of a Grignard reagent ($C_6H_5CH_2MgX$) from a halide, reaction of this Grignard reagent with the highly reactive cyclic ether, ethylene oxide, to give an adduct which is readily hydrolyzed to 3-phenyl-1-propanol. It is not necessary to isolate either the Grignard reagent or the product of the reaction between a Grignard reagent and ethylene oxide, an additional advantage which makes this method attractive.

Additional decisions would have to be made by the experimenter before laboratory work could be initiated. Since alkyl iodides are usually too expensive and less readily available than chlorides or bromides, a choice between $C_6H_5CH_2Cl$ and $C_6H_5CH_2Br$ would be necessary. In general, chlorides are less expensive but are known to be more sluggish in the Grignard reaction than are bromides. The literature should reveal yields obtained with these benzyl halides in other similar Grignard reactions. The literature should also supply such information as suitable solvents, reaction conditions, and miscellaneous information of value in carrying out the synthesis.

THE SYNTHESIS OF AROMATIC COMPOUNDS

Other types of problems encountered in synthetic work and the factors which must be considered in solving these problems may be illustrated in the preparation of aromatic compounds. At this point the reader may wish to refer to Chapter 5 in order to review the mechanism for aromatic substitution, one of the most important methods for introducing a group onto an aromatic ring. It may be recalled that groups present on an aromatic ring influence both the *reactivity* of the compound toward the attacking reagent and the *orientation* of the entering group, that is, the position on the ring where the entering group will attach itself.

The problem of orientation may be illustrated in the synthesis of the compound *m*-bromonitrobenzene. Its synthesis from benzene may be conceived by two routes which differ only in the sequence of reactions.

In reaction (A) the substituent, Br, is the directing group. Experience has shown that this substituent is an *ortho–para* directing group, that is, it directs the incoming group (—NO_2 in this case) primarily to positions which are one and three carbon atoms removed from it. The chief products to be expected by procedure (A) then would be:

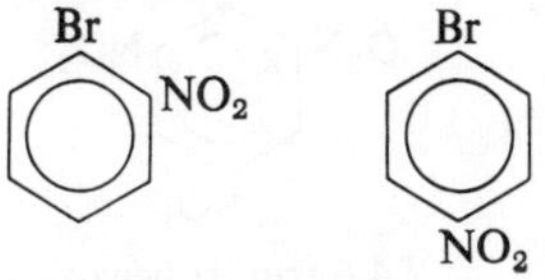

On the other hand, in reaction (B) the —NO_2 group is the directing group. It is known that this substituent is a *meta* directing group—a group which orients an incoming species to a position two carbons removed from it. It is evident, therefore, that the approach represented in equation (B) would lead to higher yields of the desired product.

Consider next the problem of the activating influence of a substituent group on the feasibility of a synthetic scheme. Following are the equations for a sequence of reactions which would appear to represent the most direct approach to the synthesis of 1,3,5-trinitro-benzene (TNB), an explosive known to have more shattering power than its relative, 2,4,6-trinitrotoluene (TNT).

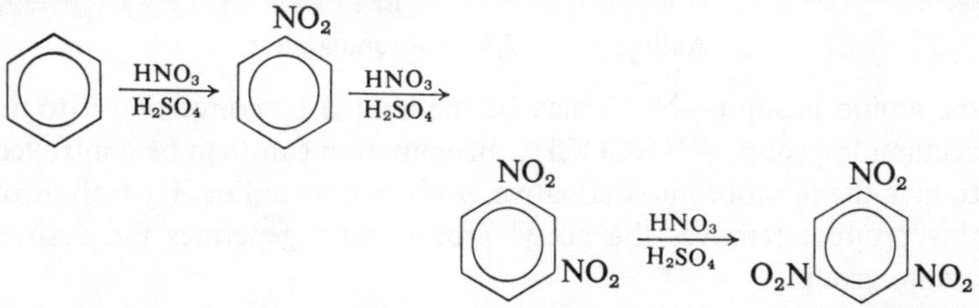

An inspection of this scheme indicates that the requirements for orientation are satisfactorily met by the *meta* orienting effect of the nitro group. However, its deactivating effect has been well demonstrated in electrophilic substitution reactions. In the final step the combined deactivating effect of the two nitro groups is sufficient to reduce the yield to the point of impracticality. To circumvent this difficulty the synthesis of TNB is accomplished in the less direct manner indicated at the top of page 100. Both the activating and orienting effect of the —CH_3 group are exploited in step one which produces TNT. In step two, oxidation of the methyl group produces the corresponding acid which can then be heated, with the loss of CO_2, to TNB.

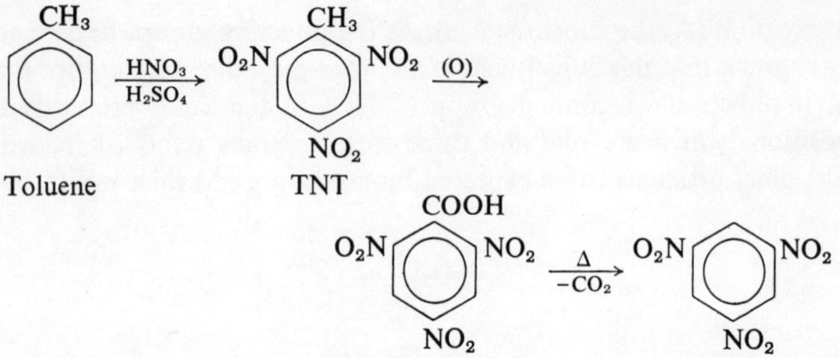

Toluene → TNT → 2,4,6-trinitrobenzoic acid → TNB

Another example of how the structure of a molecule can be modified to meet the requirements of activity and orientation is found in the synthesis of *p*-bromoaniline. Aniline is so rapidly brominated with bromine water to give 2,4,6-tribromoaniline that it is difficult to isolate the monosubstitution product. This strong activating effect of

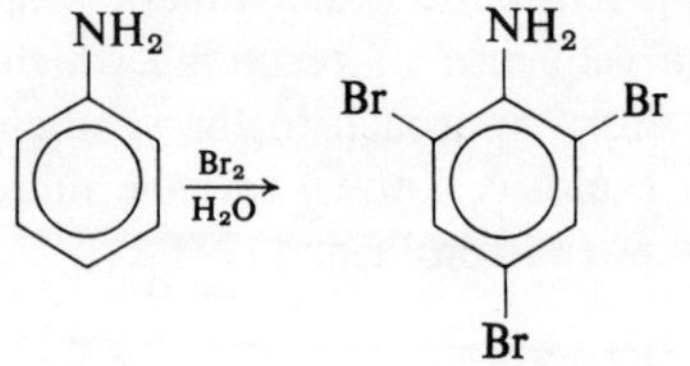

Aniline   2,4,6-tribromoaniline

the amino group (—NH$_2$) may be moderated by converting it to an acetamido group, —NHCOCH$_3$. Bromination can then be controlled to give the monobromo derivative, *p*-bromoacetanilide. Hydrolysis of this product removes the acetyl group and regenerates the desired amino group.

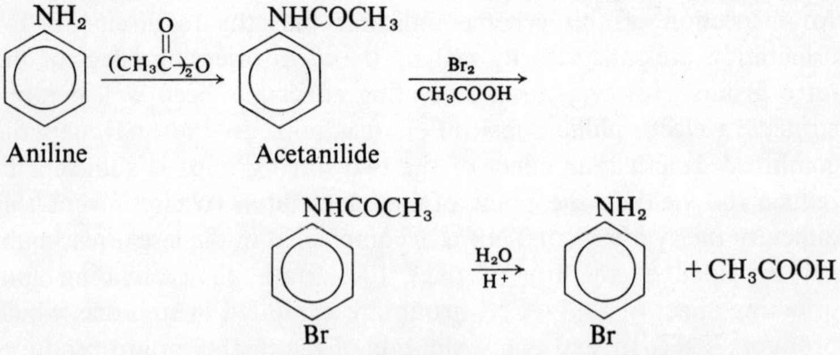

Aniline   Acetanilide

p-bromoacetanilide   *p*-bromoaniline

We shall cite one additional example of the special devices used by organic chemists to resolve problems in synthesis. The synthesis of *m*-bromophenol requires the introduction of an *ortho–para* directing group *meta* to another *ortho–para* directing group. Direct bromination of phenol is therefore not practical and an indirect approach is necessary.

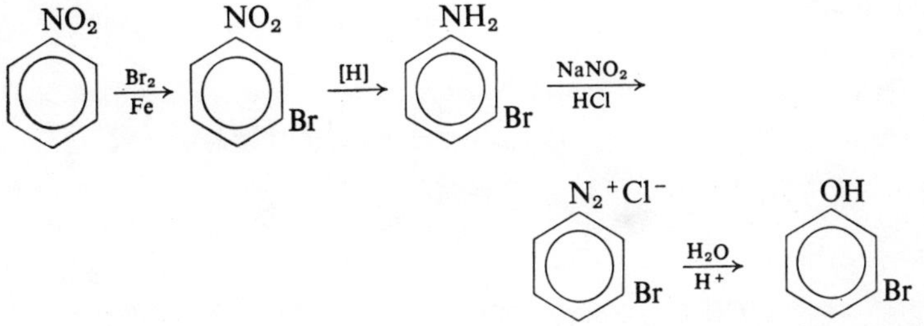

m-bromophenol

The nitro group is first used to provide the desired orientation for the bromine atom. It is then reduced to an amino group, and the amine is converted to a diazonium salt which undergoes a displacement reaction with water to give a phenol.

These are but a few of the kinds of problems which confront organic chemists who design and build molecules. Our discussion in this chapter has centered on the methods used by organic chemists to incorporate basic reactions of organic chemistry in structure design. We have attempted to be illustrative rather than comprehensive in our coverage of this very important topic. Relatively simple problems were chosen for purposes of illustration because of the limited background of most readers. Before concluding our discussion of synthesis, however, let us look briefly at some elegant synthetic achievements which testify to the great advances that have been made in constructing complex molecules.

THE SYNTHESIS OF NATURAL PRODUCTS

Nature is still the supreme architect of organic molecules although man is continually challenging this supremacy. Considering the length of time man has had to discover the intricacies of nature's architecture, it would seem he has done remarkably well in duplicating, and, in some cases, surpassing nature's accomplishments. Such complex natural substances as the antimalarial drug quinine (shown below), the tranquilizing drug reserpine (page 90) and chlorophyll-a (page 91), the pigment in plants which plays an important role in photosynthesis —all have now been fabricated by synthetic procedures. Even gigantic molecules such as natural rubber have yielded to the ingenuity of expert synthetic chemists and great strides are now being made toward constructing macromolecules resembling proteins and nucleic acids (Chapter 7).

Quinine

An appreciation of the magnitude of these feats may be partially captured in the story of the synthesis of natural rubber.

NATURAL RUBBER

Natural rubber is a polymer made up of many monomer units of the diene isoprene, CH_2=$C(CH_3)CH$=CH_2. Isoprene is one of nature's favorite building blocks and is the basic structural component of a class of naturally occurring substances called *terpenes*. Vitamin A and cholesterol are familiar examples of terpenes whose structures may be subdivided into isoprene units. These isoprene units are not linked in random fashion but are joined in a stereospecific configuration known as an all-*cis* configuration. In this arrangement the two longest carbon chains are always on the same side of the carbon–carbon double bond. *Gutta-percha* has the same molecular formula as natural rubber but has the all-*trans* configuration (p. 103). The significance of this difference in configuration is that natural rubber has physical properties far superior for most purposes to those of gutta-percha.

The first attempts to synthesize a satisfactory rubber from the monomer isoprene were unsuccessful, because the product contained isoprene units linked in random *cis* and *trans* configurations. The result

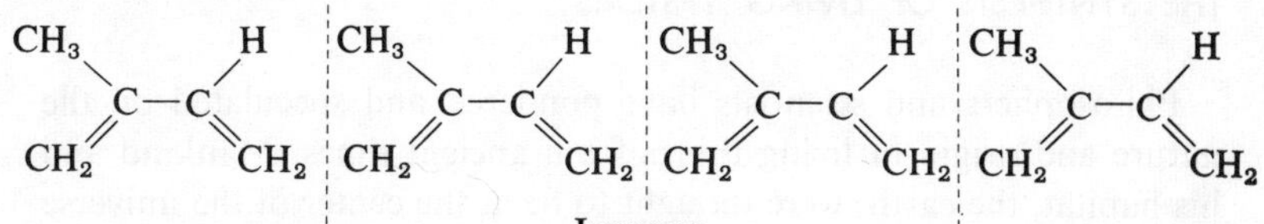

Isoprene

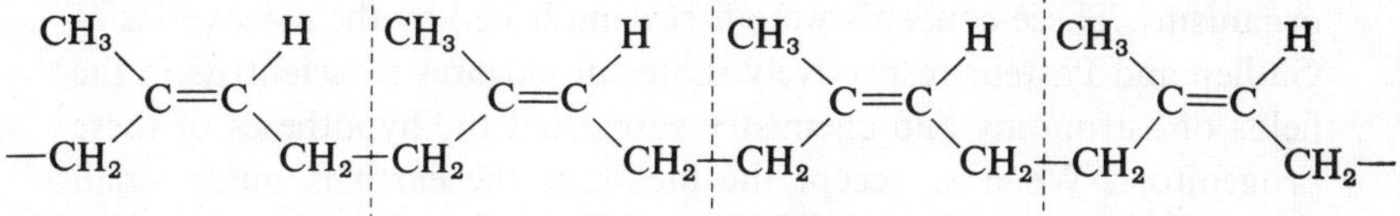

Natural Rubber

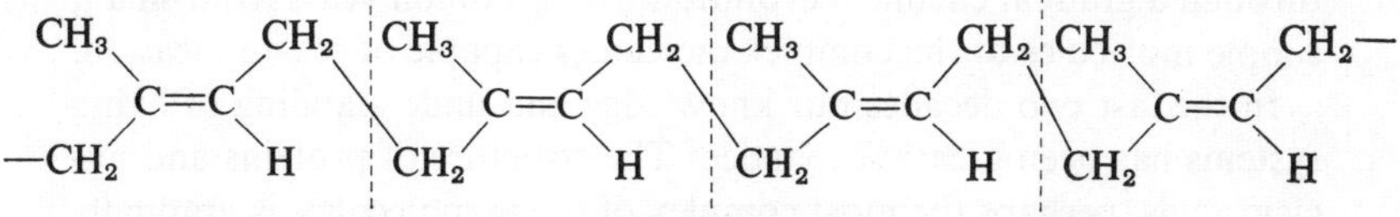

Gutta-percha

was a product of inferior quality with respect to elasticity, durability, and resistance toward oxidants and solvents. Improved synthetic rubbers were made by using dienes other than isoprene. *Neoprene* is a type of rubber made from chloroprene, $CH_2=C(Cl)CH=CH_2$. It was the first commercially successful synthetic rubber produced in the United States and, for certain uses, is still competitive with natural rubber.

The hope of synthesizing a macromolecule with an all-*cis* configuration appeared quite remote until a discovery in 1953 revolutionized the field of polymer chemistry. Karl Ziegler in Germany and Giulio Natta in Italy independently discovered and developed catalysts that permit polymerization to take place in a stereospecific manner (giving a particular geometrical isomer). The new catalysts made it possible to synthesize a rubber product from isoprene with an all-*cis* arrangement. X-ray diffraction patterns of the natural and synthetic products were nearly identical. It is still more economical to produce rubber from natural latex but the procurement of latex from the East Indies and Malay peninsula is no longer critical for the maintenance of a sufficient supply of rubber.

Many natural substances have a specificity of structure which is difficult to duplicate in the laboratory without the catalysts (enzymes) which nature employs to obtain this specificity. Stereospecific syntheses of this type represent an enormous stride in man's progress toward the fabrication of nature's molecules.

THE SYNTHESIS OF LIVING SYSTEMS

Philosophers and scientists have pondered and speculated on the nature and origin of living things from ancient times. Mankind and his habitat, the earth, were thought to be at the center of the universe and spontaneous generation was responsible for the creation of living organisms. These concepts were first demolished by the discoveries of Galileo and Pasteur respectively. Later disclosures by scientists in the fields of astronomy and chemistry supported the hypotheses of these progenitors. We now accept the fact that the earth is but a small sphere in a vast universe. Living matter is thought to have arisen through a gradual chemical evolution over a million years from small, simple molecules to the complex molecules capable of self-replication.

In the last two decades our knowledge and understanding of living systems has been greatly expanded. The structure of proteins and nucleic acids, perhaps the most complex of living molecules, is gradually unfolding. Outstanding milestones in man's attempt to unravel the mysteries of nature's architecture were: (1) the elucidation of the structure of beef insulin, a peptide (protein derivative) containing fifty-one amino acids, by Sanger at Cambridge; (2) the synthesis of oxytocin, a peptide hormone composed of eight amino acids, by duVigneaud at Cornell University; (3) the synthesis of a portion of the α-corticotropin molecule which although it contained only 23 of the total 39 amino acids in the pig hormone, had complete biological activity; (4) the synthesis of the entire α-corticotropin hormone by Schwyzer and his coworkers in Switzerland (1960); (5) the complete synthesis of bovine insulin reported by Kung in 1966.

The complete structure of the enzyme ribonuclease A was reported in 1960. A remarkable feature of this enzyme, containing 124 amino acids, is that the molecule may be severed by the enzyme subtilisin without the loss of biological activity as long as the two resulting chains are in contact with each other. When the two chains are separated, however, each chain is enzymatically inactive. Complete reactivity is restored when the two segments are reunited in a 1:1 mole ratio. The shorter of the two chains, containing 20 amino acids, has been synthesized. When this synthetic peptide is combined with the longer peptide obtained by enzymatic hydrolysis of the natural hormone, a fully active enzyme is regenerated. Synthesis of the entire ribonuclease A molecule was reported in January, 1969. We can only await the synthetic achievements of coming decades with great anticipation.

CHAPTER *7*

Giant molecules, frequently referred to as polymers, are the substance of life. The cells of animal and plant tissue are composed of an intricate network of these macromolecules, the interactions of which have only recently begun to be disclosed and understood. As they learn more about the structures of these natural molecules and the correlations between structure and properties become increasingly apparent, chemists are beginning to turn their efforts toward the design of these and similar polymers. In some instances they have been able to reproduce nature's efforts, as with synthetic rubber. In other instances they have succeeded in designing polymers for specific purposes with properties superior to those of any natural substances.

We now live in an age of plastics and recognize them as a dominating influence on our modern industrial society. Much of our clothing is made from synthetic fibers; our food is often eaten from dishes made from synthetic materials; we walk on carpets and sit on furniture made from man-made polymers. Almost every aspect of our contemporary life reflects in some way the advances made in the synthesis of giant molecules. We shall describe in this chapter some of the progress in our understanding of the structure of macromolecules. Hopefully, we may integrate some of the principles of structure and properties discussed in earlier chapters.

NATURAL POLYMERS

Carbohydrates

Carbohydrates, along with proteins and fats, are one of the important sources of food for the animal body. Chemically, they are polyhydroxy aldehydes or ketones which may exist as relatively simple

105

sugars (monosaccharides) or as enormous polymers of these simple sugars (polysaccharides). In nature the most common carbohydrates are polymers of D-glucose. (See Figure 7–1.) These polymers are known as *cellulose* and *starch*.

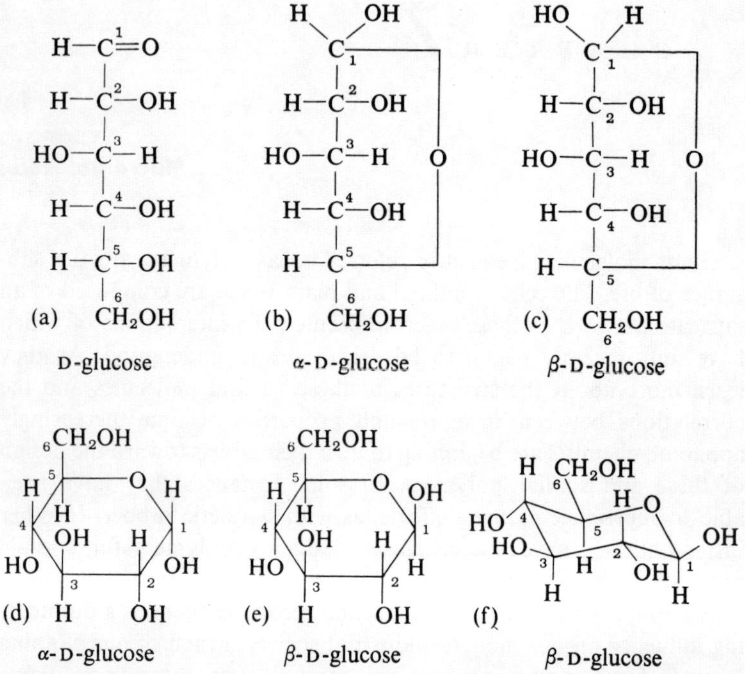

Figure 7–1 (a) A linear formula for the carbohydrate sugar D-glucose; (b) and (c) two stereoisomers of glucose which are present in equilibrium with the linear form when D-glucose is dissolved in water; (d) and (e) the same two structures represented by Haworth formulas; (f) the chair conformation of β-D-glucose showing the most stable arrangement of the *functional groups* attached to the 6-membered ring.

Cellulose

Cellulose is one of the most abundant carbohydrate polymers. It is the fibrous, structural material of plants which gives them both their shape and their strength. As shown in Figure 7–2, cellulose consists of many β-D-glucose units linked together by an oxygen atom which joins carbon atoms one and four of successive glucose units. The molecular weight of cellulose varies with the source, ranging from 250,000 to 1,000,000 or more. One molecule of cellulose, therefore,

106

contains about 1500 glucose units. By a method known as end-group analysis, the details of which are beyond the scope of this presentation, it can be determined that nearly 1000 of these units form a continuous chain, the remainder branching off from the main chain through oxygen linkages involving the one and six carbon atoms.

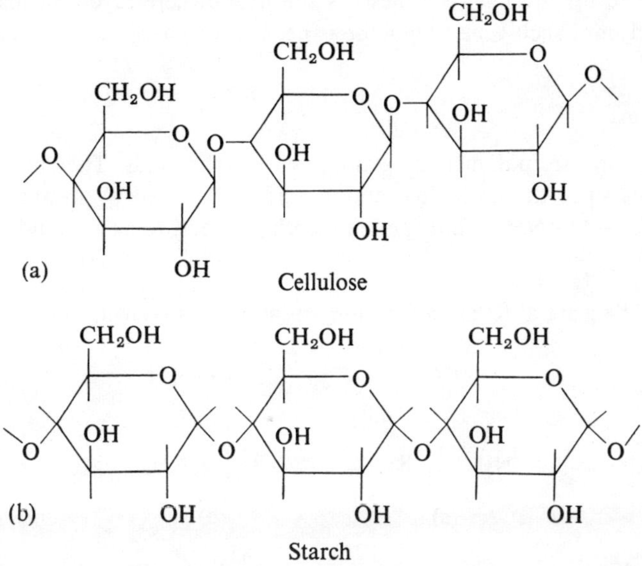

Figure 7–2 (a) An illustration of a portion of a cellulose chain with β-glucosidic linkage between glucose units; (b) A similar representation of part of a starch or glycogen chain showing α-glucosidic bonds between the one and four carbon atoms.

X-ray analysis indicates that cellulose molecules lie side by side in parallel strands. They are undoubtedly held together by hydrogen bonds linking —OH groups in neighboring strands. The visible fibers in wood are bundles of these strands twisted to form cellulose ropes.

Starch

As seen in Figure 7–2, starch is also a polymer of D-glucose but with some distinct structural differences. Hydrolysis of starch ultimately produces α-D-glucose. The glucose units are linked through α-glucosidic bonds rather than β-glucosidic bonds. Though this structural variation may at first seem inconsequential, it is nevertheless of great biological importance. Except for a few creatures such as ruminants and termites, animals are unable to utilize cellulose for

107

food, because they lack the necessary hydrolytic enzymes. On the other hand, starch is readily degraded to glucose in the digestive tract. Glucose is then absorbed through the walls of the small intestine into the blood stream. The storage form of glucose is the polymer *glycogen*, which, like starch, has α-glucosidic linkages between glucose units. The site for glycogen synthesis is the liver, where glycogen may be stored until such time as glucose is needed for energy.

Proteins

Proteins are polymers of α-amino carboxylic acids. They are polyamides since the individual amino acids are joined by means of an amide (—C—NH—) linkage, frequently referred to as a peptide link-
$$\underset{O}{\overset{\|}{}}$$
age. The general formula for an α-amino acid is shown.

(a)   (b)

It can be seen that the α-carbon atom (adjacent to the carboxyl group) is asymmetric and that two nonsuperimposable configurations (a) and (b) are therefore possible. The amino acids isolated from the hydrolysis of proteins have been found to have the specific configuration shown in (a). In this configuration when the carboxyl group is placed uppermost, the amino group is on the left relative to the hydrogen atom. Twenty amino acids, differing in the nature of the R group, are commonly obtained by the hydrolysis of protein molecules.

To understand completely the structure of a protein molecule it is necessary to consider four levels of structural organization, a complexity not encountered in simpler molecules. The *primary* structure of a protein is concerned with the manner in which amino acid residues are linked together in the formation of long chains containing peptide bonds. The arrangement of these peptide chains to form sheets or helical coils constitutes the *secondary* structure. When these coils are bent or folded or otherwise entwined, a third aspect of their structure, the *tertiary* structure, must be explained. One speaks of the *quaternary* structure of proteins when one considers the arrangement of polypeptide subunits into larger superstructures. We shall attempt to explain and illustrate these structural levels with the protein molecule hemoglobin.

Hemoglobin

Hemoglobin is the protein found in red blood cells which is responsible for oxygen transport in the blood. It is called a *conjugated* protein because the polypeptide portion (globin) is attached to an iron-containing *prosthetic* group, *heme*. These structural features are schematically summarized in the formula below. The nitrogen atoms attached to the iron atom are part of a complex ring system similar to that for chlorophyll-a.

With a molecular weight of about 67,000, an adult human hemoglobin molecule consists of four peptide chains to each of which is bound a heme group. Normal hemoglobin contains two α and two β chains, which may be isolated by removing the heme at an acidic pH followed by chromatography or electrophoresis. These four chains are apparently held together by polar and ionic forces since no evidence has yet been found to indicate any covalent binding. The complete amino acid sequence of the α and β chains has been reported; the α chain contains 141 amino acid residues and the β chain 146 residues.

The primary structure of hemoglobin can be illustrated by showing a portion of the α chain. The first three amino acids are valine, leucine, and serine. X-ray studies of peptides indicate that the —NH and

Valine   Leucine   Serine

C=O groups are coplanar. The side chains which differ for each amino acid extend in either direction from this plane. Chemical or enzymatic hydrolysis cleaves the amide linkage to give the individual amino acids.

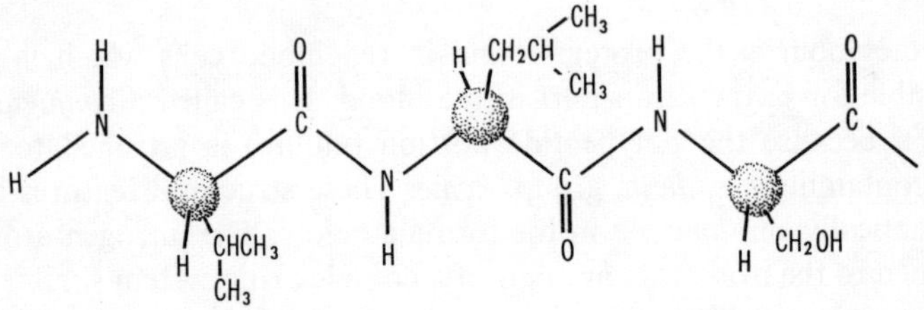

The secondary structure of hemoglobin, that is, the way in which the peptide chain is folded and bent, may be described as an α helix. The formation of the α helix may be visualized by imagining the peptide chain to be wound about an invisible rod in spiral fashion. The diameter of the rod and the pitch of the helix are such that approximately four amino acids are required to make a complete turn. Giving stability to the helical structure are hydrogen bonds uniting C=O to —NH groups in adjacent turns of the helix. A model of the α helix is illustrated in Figure 7–3.

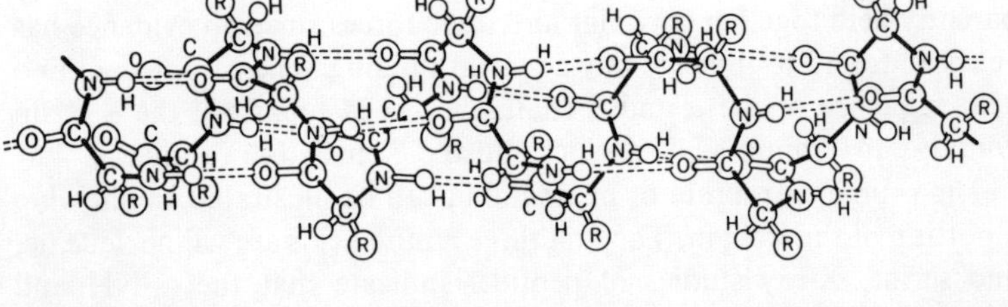

Figure 7–3 Side view of a model of an α helix similar to the configuration of the peptide chain found in hemoglobin. Hydrogen bonding is demonstrated by dotted lines linking C=O and NH groups. In this model a maximum number of hydrogen bonds is formed and the atoms comprising the peptide bond assume their normal planar configuration. From *Modern Topics in Biochemistry*, T. Bennett, E. Frieden, Macmillan Co., New York, N.Y., 1966, p. 31.

The stabilization effect of these internal hydrogen bonds is insufficient to prevent uncoiling of the α helix in water solution. Additional linkages of the helical coils resulting in folding and bending of the structure are required to furnish this additional stability. This tertiary structure involves all of the various types of bonds with which the reader is familiar—ionic bonds ($-NH_3^+$ and $-COO^-$), covalent bonds ($-S-S-$), hydrogen bonds ($-OH$ and $-COOH$), and other intermolecular forces (cf. Chapter 3). Outstanding work by J. C. Kendrew and M. Perutz has contributed to expanding our knowledge of the tertiary structure of hemoglobin and its close relative, myoglobin. Figure 7–4 illustrates the Perutz model of hemoglobin as determined by X-ray crystallography and mathematical analysis (Fourier synthesis).

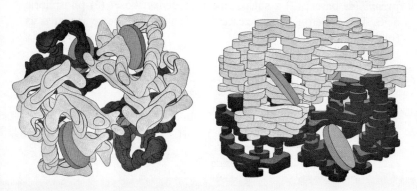

Figure 7–4 Front (left) and side (right) views of the hemoglobin molecule as proposed by Perutz. The four chains arranged in tetrahedral fashion consist of two α (light blocks) and two β (dark blocks) chains. Each disk represents a heme group. (From *Scientific American*, November, 1964.)

The quaternary structure of hemoglobin refers to the larger super-structure formed by the subunits (individual α and β chains). For hemoglobin this superstructure is thought to be a tetrahedron. Other quaternary structures which have been found for proteins are spheres and hollow tubes or rods.

Nucleic Acids

Let us now conclude our discussion of natural polymers with a brief description of nucleic acids and some of the biological implications related to their structure. The importance of nucleic acids may be inferred from their genetic role in the transmittal of hereditary information from generation to generation and their participation in the biosynthesis of proteins.

Essentially two kinds of nucleic acids are known: deoxyribonucleic acid (DNA), found primarily in the nucleus of a cell, and ribonucleic acid (RNA), located in the ribosomes and cytoplasm of the cell. The function of DNA is the transmission of hereditary information embodied in its structure. As we shall see, it can reproduce itself and act as a template for the synthesis of RNA. On the other hand, RNA translates the message obtained from DNA into thousands of proteins that are a part of the living cell.

Primary Structure. Nucleic acids are polyesters whose component parts may be divided into three classes of compounds: (1) *purine* or *pyrimidine* bases; (2) a sugar, ribose or deoxyribose; (3) phosphoric acid. The skeleton of nucleic acid molecules may be represented as follows:

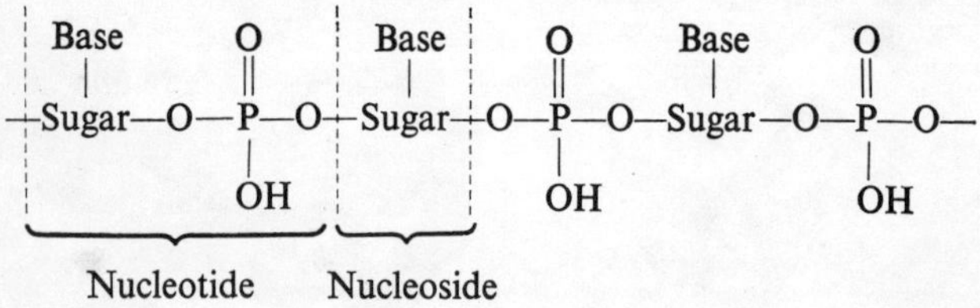

Subunits containing a base, sugar, and a phosphate residue are called *nucleotides*; a base-sugar unit is referred to as a *nucleoside*.

Several structural differences exist between DNA and RNA:

1. The sugar unit in DNA is deoxyribose which has one less —OH group than ribose, the sugar component of RNA (see Figure 7–5).

2. The four principal bases found in DNA are the purines adenine and guanine and the pyrimidines cytosine and thymine (see Figure 7–5). In RNA the first three bases are also present but thymine is replaced by uracil.

3. The molecular weight of DNA approaches 100 million whereas that of RNA is approximately one million.

A more complete picture of how the structural components of nucleic acids are combined is illustrated in Figure 7–6. The backbone of the molecule is provided by the sugar units linked through phosphate ester bonds. The purine and pyrimidine bases are side chain extensions from this backbone.

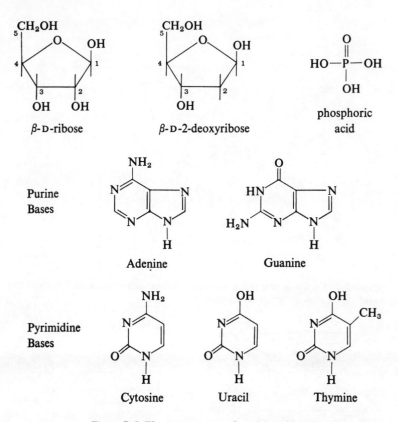

Figure 7–5 The components of nucleic acids.

The Secondary Structure. More is known at present about the secondary structure of DNA than of RNA. Analysis of the base content of DNA has shown a striking similarity in the quantities of purine-pyrimidine pairs—a 1:1 mole ratio between thymine and adenine and between cytosine and guanine. The construction of models by Watson and Crick at Cambridge University revealed that a double-stranded helix, with bases in one strand paired with complementary bases in the other strand through hydrogen bonding, could most easily explain this 1:1 ratio. These relationships are portrayed in Figure 7–7.

An understanding of the biological properties of DNA is also a consequence of the Watson-Crick model. These scientists suggested that the separate strands of DNA uncouple through the breaking of the hydrogen bonds between the paired bases. At the same time, free deoxynucleotides in the cell attach themselves to the separated strands.

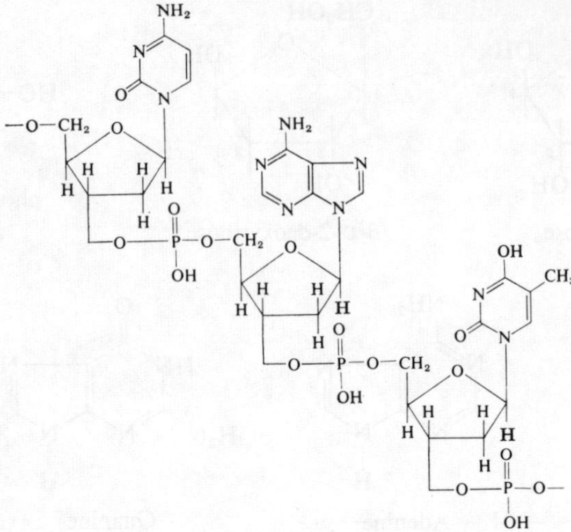

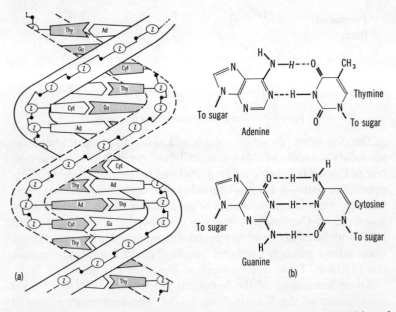

Figure 7–6 A portion of a DNA molecule schematically represented to show the bonding between structural components.

Figure 7–7 (a) The double-stranded helix showing schematically the pairing of the purine and pyrimidine bases; (b) Representation of hydrogen bonding between adenine and thymine and between guanine and cytosine. (From Karlson, P., *Introduction to Modern Biochemistry*, 2nd ed., Academic Press, N.Y. 1965.)

114

Each strand acts as a template to which the complementary base components attach. The result is that two original strands of the parent DNA molecule are now part of two identical daughter DNA molecules. The replication process may then be repeated. The Watson-Crick hypothesis for DNA replication is strongly supported by experimental evidence which, because of space limitations, cannot be presented here. (Cf. reference (1).)

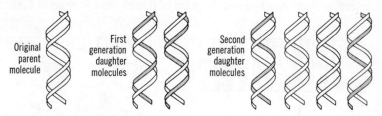

Figure 7–8 An illustration of the self-replication of DNA as proposed by Watson and Crick.

THE BIOSYNTHESIS OF PROTEINS

We have noted earlier that the function of RNA, of which there are several different types, is the translation of the message embodied in the DNA molecule for the synthesis of proteins. In recent years the mechanism of this biosynthesis has been partially elucidated.

The amino acid to be incorporated into the protein is first *activated*. This is necessary because proteins can not be synthesized by a simple reversal of the protein hydrolysis procedure. The activating agent is adenosine triphosphate (ATP), which forms an anhydride linkage with the carboxyl group of the amino acid with the liberation of pyrophosphate (P-P). Schematically,

$$\text{AA} + \text{ATP} \xrightarrow{\text{enzyme}} \underset{\substack{\text{Activated} \\ \text{amino acid}}}{\text{AA-AMP}} + \underset{\text{Pyrophosphate}}{\text{P-P}}$$

The activated amino acid is then transferred to a specific RNA called *transfer* RNA (*t*-RNA). There is at least one *t*-RNA for each amino

$$\text{AA-AMP} + t\text{-RNA} \xrightarrow{\text{enzyme}} \text{AA-}t\text{-RNA} + \text{AMP}$$

acid. The transfer RNA with its attached amino acid migrates to a ribosome where it becomes attached to a larger RNA called *messenger*

---

[1] James D. Watson, *The Double Helix,* Atheneum Press.

RNA (*m*-RNA). The order of the attachment of the amino-acid-bearing *t*-RNA's is dictated by the base-sequence in the *m*-RNA which in turn has been "copied" from DNA. It is believed that a sequence of three nucleotide bases in the *m*-RNA constitutes a "codon" for the binding of an AA-*t*-RNA. After alignment on the surface of the ribosome, the amino acids are joined enzymatically and the resulting protein is detached from the transfer RNA's and is free to carry on its cell activity. A schematic diagram of this process is given in Figure 7–9.

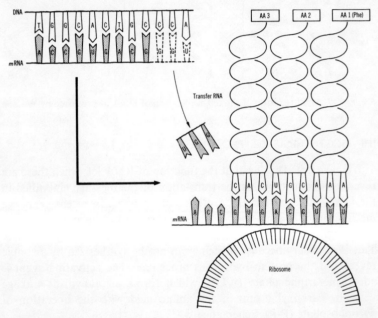

Figure 7–9 Diagram showing the steps in protein biosynthesis: synthesis of *m*-RNA at DNA from where it moves to the ribosome; pairing of base codon in *m*-RNA with the complementary codon in *t*-RNA; linking of the amino acids to form peptide chain. (Diagram from Karlson's *Introduction to Modern Biochemistry*, 2nd Ed., Academic Press, New York, N.Y., 1965.)

SYNTHETIC POLYMERS

A hint of the progress made in synthetic polymer chemistry since its inception in the early 1920's was given in Chapter 6 in the discussion relating to synthetic rubber. Following a short description of the chemical methods used to create polymers we shall illustrate the structural features of some of the giant molecules which the reader may recognize by their more familiar "household" names. We shall then point out some correlations between the structure and the observed properties of the polymers.

The Preparation of Polymers

Polymers may be conveniently classified into two general types— *addition* polymers and *condensation* polymers. In addition polymerization, monomer units are added progressively without any loss of atoms occurring during the attachment of one monomer unit to another. The total molecular weight of the polymer is the sum of the molecular weights of the monomer components incorporated in the molecule. In condensation polymerization, on the other hand, interaction of monomer units is accompanied by the elimination of a small molecule such as water or ethyl alcohol.

Addition
Polymerization: $n\,CH_2{=}CH_2 \longrightarrow$
 Ethylene

 $\sim\!\!\sim CH_2{-}CH_2{-}CH_2{-}CH_2{-}CH_2{-}CH_2\!\!\sim\!\!\sim$ or $-\!\!\left(CH_2{-}CH_2\right)_{\overline{n}}$
 Polyethylene

Condensation
Polymerization: $H_2N(CH_2)_6NH_2 + HOOC(CH_2)_4COOH \longrightarrow$
 Hexamethylene Adipic Acid
 diamine

$$\left[-NH(CH_2)_6NH\overset{\overset{\textstyle O}{\|}}{C}(CH_2)_4\overset{\overset{\textstyle O}{\|}}{C} \right]_n + 2nH_2O$$
 Nylon 66

Many important addition polymerization reactions occur with molecules which are alkenes or dienes. The reaction is initiated by a free radical or an ion (either cation or anion). A chain reaction follows in which the macromolecule is formed, termination occurring when the giant free radical (or ion) combines with another free radical (or ion). These two mechanisms are illustrated in the formation of polyethylene. (See p. 118.)

In the polymerization of isoprene to form synthetic rubber (Table 7–1) the isoprene units join end to end in similar fashion. An

FREE RADICAL POLYMERIZATION

Peroxide $\rightarrow$ R· (free radical)

$$R· + CH_2{=}CH_2 \longrightarrow RCH_2CH_2· \xrightarrow{CH_2=CH_2} RCH_2CH_2CH_2CH_2·$$

$$\xrightarrow{CH_2=CH_2} RCH_2CH_2CH_2CH_2CH_2CH_2· \ldots \text{ etc.}$$

$$\xrightarrow{R·} RCH_2CH_2CH_2CH_2CH_2CH_2 \ldots R$$
Polyethylene

CATIONIC POLYMERIZATION

$$R^+ + CH_2{=}CH_2 \longrightarrow RCH_2CH_2{}^+ \xrightarrow{CH_2=CH_2} RCH_2CH_2CH_2CH_2{}^+$$

$$\xrightarrow{CH_2=CH_2} RCH_2CH_2CH_2CH_2CH_2CH_2{}^+ \ldots \text{ etc.}$$

$$\xrightarrow{R^-} RCH_2CH_2CH_2CH_2CH_2CH_2 \ldots R$$
Polyethylene

important difference in this polymer is that a double bond is retained in each isoprene unit. We also noted that it is necessary for polymerization to take place in a stereospecific manner so that the arrangement of groups around the carbon–carbon double bond is all-*cis*. For a more complete introduction to stereospecific polymerization the reader is referred to an article by Dr. G. Natta (2), one of the pioneers in stereospecific polymerization.

Typical of the type of reaction involved in condensation polymerization is the formation of Nylon 66. In the preparation of this polymer, adipic acid and hexamethylenediamine first react to form a salt.

Table 7–1

Addition Polymers

Trade name	Monomer Formula and Name	Polymer Structure	Use
Polythene Polyethylene	$CH_2{=}CH_2$, ethylene	$\text{---}(CF_2{-}CF_2)_n\text{---}$	Plastic bottles and containers, molded toys.
Teflon	$CF_2{=}CF_2$, tetrafluoroethylene	$\text{---}(CH_2{-}CH_2)_n\text{---}$	Nonsticking, water-repellant, stain-resistant, chemically inert coatings.
Polystyrene Styron Styrofoam	$C_6H_5CH{=}CH_2$, styrene	$\left(CH_2{-}\underset{\underset{C_6H_5}{\shortmid}}{CH}\right)_n$	Electrical insulation, foamed plastic materials.
Saran	$CH_2{=}CCl_2$, vinylidene chloride	$\left(CH_2{-}\underset{\underset{Cl}{\overset{Cl}{\shortmid}}}{\overset{\shortmid}{C}}\right)_n$	Wrapping and packaging materials, seat covers.

(2) "Precisely Constructed Polymers," G. Natta, *Scientific American*, August, 1961.

When the salt is heated under reduced pressure, water is eliminated and the polymer is formed. (Cf. amide formation in Chapter 5.) Tables 7–1 and 7–2 illustrate the structural features of some addition and condensation polymers, the trade names of which have become a part of our every day vocabulary.

STRUCTURE vs. PROPERTIES

Why does rubber stretch and then resume its shape when the tension is released? Why are Polythene and Teflon chemically inert to solvents and oxidizing agents? What similarities exist between Nylon and Orlon which make them useful as fibers and fabrics? The search for the answers to these and other questions related to polymer structure and their applications has occupied polymer chemists for several decades. Many polymer chemists now feel that research in this field has developed to the point where it is possible to tailor-make a polymer for a specific application. Let us examine some of the correlations which have been made between the structure and properties of macromolecules.

Chemical Inertness

To be chemically inert a polymer normally must have unreactive functional groups. Under some circumstances a polymer having reactive functional groups may remain inert if those functional groups are "hidden" within the structure of the macromolecule so that they can not be attacked. Polyethylene contains only C—H and C—C bonds. Like most hydrocarbons, this polymer is unreactive because C—H and C—C bonds are not easily attacked except by free radicals. Even more inert is the polymer Teflon, in which C—F bonds replace the C—H bonds in polyethylene. Carbon–fluorine bonds are among the strongest chemical bonds known. The larger F atoms also shield the C—C bonds from attack. Thus, Teflon can be heated to 600°F without melting; it can also be used as a lining in tanks of nitric and sulfuric acids. Even temporary bonds with other compounds are not easily formed so that Teflon possesses nonsticking characteristics.

Crystallinity

Molecules which have repeating structural features that can fit into a crystal lattice may be described as *crystalline*. In contrast, materials whose components are arranged in random fashion are *amorphous*.

Table 7–2

Condensation Polymers

Trade name	Monomer Formula and Name	Polymer Structure	Use
Melmac	Melamine NH_2 ... N, N, N, NH_2, H_2N and $CH_2{=}O$	(Structure uncertain)	Laminates for counter tops, dinnerware.
Epoxy resin	Bisphenol A (NaO–C$_6$H$_4$–C(CH$_3$)$_2$–C$_6$H$_4$–ONa) and Epichlorohydrin (CH_2–CHCH$_2$Cl, O)	Structure with bisphenol A unit and OCH_2CHCH_2 / OH	Adhesives, surface coatings.
Dacron	Dimethyl terephthalate (CH_3OOC–C$_6$H$_4$–$COOCH_3$) and Ethylene glycol ($HOCH_2CH_2OH$)	Structure with terephthalate and CH_2CH_2O	Magnetic tapes, fibers, fabrics.

120

Polymers in which a stereospecific orientation exists, such as those prepared by Natta and Ziegler (page 103), have a greater degree of crystallinity than molecules having less regular structural features. Bulkiness in functional groups attached to the main polymer chain contributes to a greater degree of amorphous character. Crystalline polymers frequently have higher densities, greater tensile strength, higher melting points, and are less soluble than amorphous polymers.

Elasticity

Polymers which have elastic character are known as *elastomers*. Stretching may be attributed to the fact that part of the molecule is free to move. To resume its original shape the polymer must also contain part of its chain length in fixed positions. To accomplish this optimum condition of rigidity and flexibility the polymer chains must be joined by cross-links. Rubber, for example, must be vulcanized to form —S—S— links between chains in order to obtain the proper balance of rigidity and flexibility. Increasing the number of cross-links provides greater strength and toughness. Ebonite, the hard type of rubber found in battery cases, has been vulcanized until the stretching property has been essentially removed. Bakelite and Glyptal resins are also examples of such *network polymers*.

Fibers

Fibers are generally linear molecules with a rather pronounced degree of crystallinity. Nylon 66, as we have seen, is a linear polyamide. Polymers which are to be made into fibers used in textiles must have high tensile strength; they must have high enough melting points to withstand the temperatures of ironing. They must be insoluble in dry cleaning solvents but soluble in solvents from which they may be extruded and spun. Some cross-linking is necessary to furnish the required rigidity and strength.

A unique example of designing and developing a man-made fiber may be found in the evolution of spandex, the stretch fiber used in ski suits, bathing suits, and women's undergarments. The story of spandex began with the search of William Charch, a Du Pont polymer chemist, for a rubber-like polymer strong enough to be drawn into a fiber. With the skill of a molecular architect he blended into a polymer molecules which imparted the exact qualities of stretch and resiliency which he sought. These qualities may be imagined in the structural components of spandex shown on page 22.

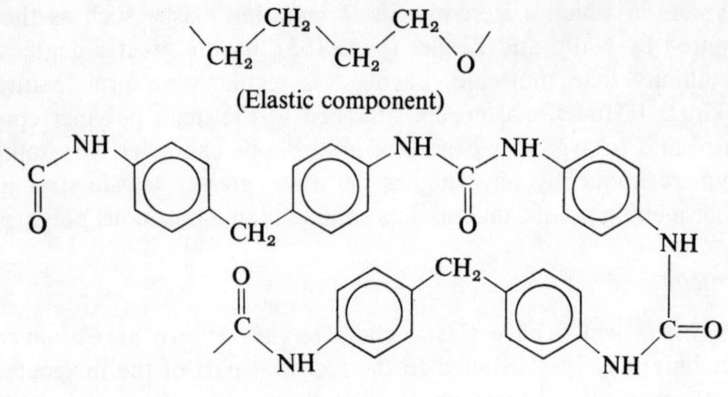

$$\text{(Elastic component)}$$

(Elastic component)

(Fiber component)

FUTURE DEVELOPMENTS

What will the new generation of space-age synthetics be like? Already promising new polymers are in stages of development and testing, their full potential yet to be realized. Lexan (or Merlon) is a transparent polyester so strong that a quarter inch sheet will not break under the blow of a sledge hammer or be penetrated by a 0.38 caliber bullet fired from a distance of twelve feet. A silicone polymer, RTV 615, has the properties of a synthetic rubber; yet it withstands temperatures of 15,000°F and has been tested as a heat shield for space vehicles during reentry. Tests performed on Eastman 910, a liquid adhesive formed by the polymerization of $CH_2{=}C(CN)COOCH_3$, reveal that it will bond two solids into a virtually permanent union. A Du Pont plastic, Kapton, is so stable that it remains unaffected by temperatures ranging from $-425°F$ to $752°F$. Mylar is another Du Pont discovery which is so tough that a thrown baseball will bounce off a film 0.001-inch thick. No longer does the word "synthetic" connote an inferior substance made as a cheap substitute for a natural product. For a graphic preview of these and other promising synthetics the reader should consult the excellent pictorial essays in the book, *Giant Molecules* (3). An excellent discussion of the relationship between polymer structure and properties may be found in reference (4).

---

[3] H. F. Mark, *Giant Molecules*, Time Inc., New York, N.Y., 1966, a volume in the Life Science Library.

[4] C. C. Price, "The Effect of Structure on Chemical and Physical Properties of Polymers," *J. Chem. Educ.*, **42**, 13 (1965).

Index

Abandoned Seas: Reversing the Decline of the Oceans

PETER WEBER

Anne Platt, *Staff Researcher*

Ed Ayres, *Editor*

WORLDWATCH PAPER 116
November 1993

PUBLICATIONS of the Institute include the annual *State of the World*, which is now published in 27 languages; *Vital Signs*, an annual compendium of the global trends—environmental, economic, and social—that are shaping our future; the *Environmental Alert* book series; and *World Watch* magazine, as well as the *Worldwatch Papers*. For more information on Worldwatch publications, write: Worldwatch Institute, 1776 Massachusetts Ave., N.W., Washington, DC 20036; or FAX (202) 296-7635.

THE WORLDWATCH PAPERS provide in-depth, quantitative and qualitative analysis of the major issues affecting prospects for a sustainable society. The Papers are authored by members of the Worldwatch Institute research staff and reviewed by experts in the field. Published in five languages, they have been used as a concise and authoritative reference by governments, nongovernmental organizations and educational institutions worldwide. For a partial list of available Papers, see page 67.